Peter Marsh

THE ROBOT AGE

First published in Great Britain
in the Abacus imprint 1982 by
Sphere Books Ltd
30–32 Gray's Inn Road, London WC1X 8JL
Copyright © Peter Marsh 1982

Typeset by Inforum Ltd, Portsmouth
Printed and bound in Great Britain by
Collins, Glasgow

Peter Marsh is author of *The Silicon Chip Book*, available in Abacus, and is currently Industry Editor for the *New Scientist*.

Contents

Part One: The Road to the Robot Factory
1 The importance of making things   3
2 Automation – what it means   9
3 Four industrial revolutions   18

Part Two: The Legacy of the Past
4 The age of mechanisation, 1760–1840   25
5 The start of mass production, 1880–1920   35
6 Enter the computer, 1940–1980   44

Part Three: The Robot Age
7 Anatomy of a robot   59
8 Robots march in   65
9 The seeing machine   82
10 Tomorrow's factory   96

Part Four: The Robot Future
11 Machines that think: artificial intelligence   117
12 Beyond automation   122
13 Factories in space   137
14 The robot breeder   146

Part Five: Lessons
15 The Japanese experience   155
16 What future for Britain?   168

Books and reports consulted   179

TABLES

1	Machines through the ages	12
2	Growth in demand of manufactured products	97
3	Market forecasts for computerised manufacturing equipment	113
4	Change in employment structure, Japan and Britain, 1973–79	162
5	Performance in manufacturing industry, Japan and Britain, 1973–79	163
6	Fixed investment as proportion of GNP – different nations	165
7	Share of major countries in industrialised world's manufactured exports	165
8	Industrial R&D spending – different countries	169
9	Industrial R&D spending – Britain	169
10	British government spending on R&D – 1972–81	170
11	Kay/Forsyth argument on North Sea oil's effect on UK economy	172
12	Alternative scheme for mid 1980s economy	173
13	Britain's exports and imports, 1979	175

FIGURES

1	Human and artificial feedback	17
2	1956 concept of automatic factory	46
3	Anatomy of a robot	68
4	Robot with rudimentary vision	87
5	Evolution of computerised manufacturing systems	103
6	Japanese automated factory	108
7	Possible layout of computer-controlled factory	109
8	Computer power and computer energy of various devices	135
9	Plan of space factory	144
10	Self-replicating robot	147
11	Plan of "breeder" factory	149
12	Exponential growth of self-replicating Moon factory	150
13	Mobile universal construction unit for space factory	151
14	Workers in sectors of employment - international comparisons	161

PART 1

The Road to the Robot Factory

Chapter One
The importance of making things

This book is about making things – in the past, now and in the future. Turn your thoughts just for the moment to the future, to the year 2050. Imagine you are a countryside dweller somewhere in the developed western world. Living in your pleasant rural retreat, you rarely want or need to travel very far. Of course, you are familiar with the products of the industries of the big cities; how could you be otherwise when you spend so much of your salary on them and never fail to marvel at their variety and sophistication? But you know virtually nothing about how they are made.

Your first question, then, as you approach one of the great industrial cities on a once-in-a-lifetime visit, is: 'Where are all the factories?' You are nonplussed by the lack of evident industrial activity. Your guide gently touches your arm and points – to a row of box-like structures that you assumed were garages.

The first thing to notice about the factories of the 21st century will be their smallness. Further, there will be fewer of them than today, and they will require only small numbers of people to operate them. Yet by working for twenty-four hours a day, for much of this time untended except by a few maintenance men, the factories will turn out all the goods to meet the increasingly sophisticated tastes of the communities around them.

How this will happen is the subject of this book.

But new manufacturing technology does not become important overnight, nor in a few years for that matter. Since the dawn of civilisation, people have struggled to make things more efficiently. Making things has always been important. For the ancient peoples around the Mediterranean, the technology – not just the art – of constructing pots from clay was highly valued. The remains of neolithic axe factories on the windswept hillsides of southern England testify to the importance to early mankind of shaping things out of stone.

Over the years, people melded technology with organisation to make things to a higher standard and at less cost. The Romans who invaded Britain knew that their subjects would work better at hammering objects out of bits of metal if they were organised into small groups, instead of working away on their own. In the 18th century, Britain carried on the Roman tradition to its logical conclusion. By combining technical advances with ruthless exploitation of workers, the country became the first to industrialise and won a vital economic advantage over the rest of the world, the effects of which are still reverberating through factory floors (and elsewhere) today.

In much of the developed world, technologists and business people are trying, as they have done for centuries, to make things with fewer workers. The name of the enterprise is still the substitution of machines for muscles. Manufacturers are aiming to cut costs, to take people out of nasty environments and to make objects to a better standard.

Making these goals achievable is a string of impressive technical advances concerning computers and automated systems such as industrial robots. This book will explain these advances. But the changes taking place concern not only technology. Behind them is another factor – which can be labelled only as economic warfare.

With the world more than ever before an international market place, in which every country is trying to undercut or outsell its rivals, there is immense pressure on businesses to increase their competitiveness by introducing advanced machinery. The rise of Japan as the world's most successful manufacturer has sent shock waves through the western world, particularly the US. In recent years, the rise of Japan has dealt a blow to the industrial virility of America – which has grown used to thinking of itself as the world's leading manufacturing power. We are now seeing the backlash.

As one American manufacturer told me in 1981: 'We've lost our TV industry to foreigners: our auto companies are going the same way. The suits you and I are wearing probably came from Asia. It's time America did something about it.'

Companies in the US, and elsewhere, have resolved that to match Japan, they will have to borrow some of the technical innovations which that country has employed in its factories. In order to keep up

4

the pressure, they will probably have to go a lot further down the road of factory automation. This explains the rush of activity, particularly in the us, to buy automated equipment such as robots and to step up research into yet more advanced kinds of machinery.

Why should you plough through two hundred or so pages finding out how the world makes things? Everything we do is influenced by the products of manufacturing industry. Whether we are in houses, at work, walking down a road, eating a sandwich, watching a film or reading a book, we are in contact with objects made in factories.

Furthermore, the cash earned from manufacturing helps to pay – perhaps indirectly – for services such as schools, hospitals and the police. And services, of course, could not operate without manufactured products. Ask a fireman how he would put out blazes without a fire appliance – or a teacher how he would teach without books, desks and blackboards.

How a country runs its manufacturing industry will have a big effect on life in general – both economically and socially. Firms that use up-to-date technology in their factories will be successful on world markets and create wealth. Many people are concerned, however, that if technical advances go too far and too many companies replace their human workers with machines, the displaced employees will not find new jobs. With the high unemployment rates of the 1980s, the prospects for new jobs that could soak up some of the people who leave manufacturing do not look too bright.

To be sure, in the developed world, the trend that fewer people work in manufacturing industry is nothing new. In western Europe, thirty to forty per cent of the working populations have jobs in 'secondary' industry (manufacturing plus construction and mining) compared with forty to fifty per cent earlier this century.

Exactly when the 'peaks' of numbers employed in these industries occurred varies from nation to nation. It depends largely on when the country experienced its first industrial revolution, in which there was an initial large-scale transfer of workers from agriculture to manufacturing.

Being the first industrial nation, Britain was the scene of the first big shift from the fields to the factories. At the beginning of the 18th century, four-fifths of the population of some five million worked

5

on the land. By 1841, about half the country's working population had jobs in factories.

Today, some two-fifths of Britain's workforce make things in factories or work in mines or on building sites. A little under sixty per cent work in service industries, which are anything from state-run railways, schools and offices to barber's shops and firms that sell computer software or make and show films. Only a few per cent now work in 'primary' industry – fishing and farming. The figures are similar in other industrialised countries, in most of which 'secondary' employment has been declining for twenty years or more as the new service businesses prosper.

But if technical changes occur at the rate of the recent past – with economic pressures forcing factories to implement them – the proportion of countries' labour force employed in manufacturing could slump even lower within the next twenty or so years. What wider changes will this bring to the world as a whole?

To answer this question, I have tried to draw lessons from what has happened in the past. After the first part of the book, which examines the concept of 'automation' and explains what it means, Part Two (the next three chapters) considers the history of factories since the industrial revolution in Britain in the late 1700s. This historical slant is important for three reasons, I believe. Firstly, what has happened influences to some degree the likely course of events in the future. For instance, Britain is still experiencing the consequences of being the first industrial nation. Any book which seeks to explore Britain's industrial future without talking a little about events 200 years ago can be written off as a failure.

Secondly, so many books have been written over the past two centuries about 'mechanisation' and (more recently) 'automation' that a volume covering these topics should pay some attention to what its predecessors had to say. Thirdly, the history of technical change in factories is fascinating; and this is as good a reason as any for including an outline of it.

The third and fourth parts of the book concern the present and the future. They examine robots; their history and prospects; the other new kinds of computer-controlled equipment in factories, machine tools for instance; the research into advanced 'intelligent' machines that can think for themselves how to operate in workshops; how Japan has got ahead in robot development; the future for factories in the unlikely environment of space, where, in the next century, there may be yet another industrial revolution; and finally, the prospects for the UK.

Making things *is* important, as the new types of goods constantly appearing in the shops of the western world testify. Homing in on the special characteristics of Britain, however, people sometimes argue that the country is getting so bad at making things that it should withdraw from this activity (speeding up a trend that is already occurring) and concentrate on activities that it is good at – service industries. Such areas would include computer software, financial services, tourism, distribution of goods, publishing, making films and so on. Taking this scheme to its conclusion, Britain would become a nation with no factories, earning its living by trading services with the rest of the world.

Unfortunately, this scheme is unworkable. As it has to import so much of its food and raw materials, Britain has to export about twenty per cent of its gross domestic product (the nation's annual output of goods and services) to come anywhere near breaking even. In 1979, exports of commodities totalled £42 billion, of which manufactured goods came to £33 billion. The rest comprised items such as food, fuel and raw materials. Exports of services amounted to a mere £14 billion. Over the next few years, with North Sea oil, Britain will need to import very little fuel and will be a net exporter of oil. So the country will not need to sell as much overseas to pay for what it buys. But this situation will not last for ever. In the long term, the oil will dry up. The UK will then need, once more, to sell a lot of manufactured exports to offset spending on foreign goods. It is nonsense to think that services could take on the burden of providing the bulk of Britain's overseas sales.

As Sir Monty Finniston's committee of inquiry into the engineering profession put it in 1980: 'Although tourism, the financial and insurance contributions of the City of London and the traded services sector generally have long provided a surplus on their balance of payments, they have only limited capability to fund a large deficit from trade in manufactured products ... Notwithstanding the growing importance of the service sector as an employer and generator of prosperity, the long-term growth of the [British] economy depends upon the value of domestic output of manufactured goods continuing to rise to meet a substantial share of domestic demand, both to meet those demands and to earn sufficient currency from sales abroad to pay for the imports of raw materials, food, fuel, manufactured products and services.'

Britain cannot afford not to ensure that its future is bound up with manufacturing. And that means more machines in factories. It means more automation, a word with a hazy past whose time has now come.

Chapter Two
Automation – what it means

As the word 'automation' is bandied about so much nowadays, and as it will crop up often in this book, we ought to consider in detail its definition – something that has been debated for the past thirty years. For a word that is used so much, there is little common ground over what 'automation' means.

'Automation' was coined only in the late 1940s. Del Harder, an executive with the Ford car company, is credited for bringing it into the language. It obviously stems from the word 'automatic' and is probably a shortening of an earlier term, 'automatisation'. The new word came into common use in the 1950s, when there was a rash of books and magazine articles on the subject.

According to the Concise Oxford Dictionary, automation is 'the automatic control of the manufacture of a product through successive stages'. Automatic is itself defined as 'self acting'. Leonard Langdon Goodman's *Man and Automation*,* published in 1957, gives a more complete, though somewhat verbose definition: 'Automation is the technology of automatic working in which the handling methods, the processes, and the design of the processed material are integrated to utilise, as is economically justifiable, the mechanisation of thought and effort, in order to achieve automatic and, in some cases, a self-regulating chain of processes.'

Any word that is given such a long and clumsy definition is clearly open to misinterpretation. In evidence to the US Congress's 1961 inquiry into the impact of automation on unemployment, Malcolm Denise, a Ford vice-president, complained that the meaning of a term that his company had coined was 'completely out of control'. The word originally denoted a specific industrial process. Denise went on, however, 'I am disturbed . . . by the fact that automation

*Full details of books and articles referred to are given in the Appendix.

9

has taken on an additional meaning that has no relevance to real life. Although no one actually defines it in this way in so many words, automation is frequently used to mean anything that causes unemployment . . . It is easy to jump to the conclusion that the wizards of the laboratories are on the verge of making people obsolete, and, indeed, have already begun to do so. When, at the same time, unemployment rises, it is perhaps only natural to conclude that our unemployment problems are the result of automation.'

In support of his thesis, Denise quoted from James Bright's *Automation and Management*, which listed no fewer than twenty-four definitions of automation. Bright wrote: 'Few words have been so twisted to suit a number of purposes and phobias as this new word "automation". It has been used as a technological rallying cry, a manufacturing goal, an engineering challenge, an advertising slogan, a labour campaign banner and as the symbol of ominous technological progress.'

If people in the 1950s quarrelled about the meaning of the word, no one doubted that automation was the latest manifestation of a process that had been taking place for centuries – the substitution of machines for workers. In the 1950s and 1960s, people feared that a new breed of machines – what US congressman Adam Powell called 'the Frankenstein of automation' – would lead to massive unemployment. Powell's view was supported by an opinion poll in Detroit, which asked people whom or what they feared most. 'The Russians' came first and 'automation' came second.

The concern was nothing new. For at least 700 years, people have been scared of machines taking over their jobs.

In 1397, for instance, guild leaders in Cologne persuaded the town's authorities to ban a machine for making pin heads on the grounds that it would cause unemployment. In 16th century England, Parliament enacted a law that stopped cloth merchants setting up workshops with more than a set number of machines. The intention was to keep open the rights of citizens to make cloth in their own homes free from competition from capitalists.

About the same time, an inventor in Danzig called Anthony Müller devised a new kind of weaving machine for making textiles.

10

Today, such people go to the authorities for financial support because they believe they are helping the community. Support was very thin on the ground in Müller's day; fearing unemployment and the unrest this would cause, the local mayor had the hapless inventor murdered.

Later, as the Industrial Revolution got under way in England, groups of people known as Luddites went on the rampage. They demonstrated their lack of enthusiasm for the machines of the day by breaking them with hammers called 'Enochs', after the blacksmith Enoch Taylor who made them. Taylor must have been one of the most astute capitalists of the time: he could hardly lose, as he made not only the hammers but the machines that the mobs smashed. Hence the peculiar rallying call of the time: 'Enoch made them, Enoch shall break them'. But this is straying into the subject matter of Chapter 4, which will consider the Industrial Revolution in detail.

Clearly, workers of these periods were concerned not with automation – the word had not been invented – but mechanisation. To understand the first term, however, we must inquire into the second. This will also help to define exactly what people mean when they talk about the various stages of industrial change that have affected the world.

Mechanisation, or the use of machines to do the work of animals or people, has been with us for centuries, as Table 1 illustrates. The Table shows the six basic types of mechanised contraption, together with a few examples of purely human activities. The classification depends on whether machines, or combinations of animals and people, are responsible for the three fundamental elements that occur in every type of activity, human or otherwise – power, action and control.

Thus in handwriting, which is placed firmly in the 'human activities' section of the Table, the human body is responsible for all three elements. Typing, on the other hand, introduced the first kind of mechanisation. In typing these words, my body produces the power to drive a machine (the typewriter). But the machine provides 'action', in the form of bits of metal that hammer down on paper. Control remains firmly with me; the keys will not move

Table 1. Machines through the ages.

(*a version of this table first appeared in* New Scientist, *12 February 1981*)

		Device	Country responsible	Approx. date introduced	Power	Action	Control
HUMAN ACTIONS							
	Activity	Walking	—	2.5M BC	Body	Legs	Brain
		Handwriting	Egypt	3500 BC	Body	Hands	Brain
		Hand weaving	Egypt	3500 BC	Body	Hands	Brain
MECHANICAL DEVICES							
Mechanisation	Without mechanical power	Ox plough	Meso-potamia	3000 BC	Animal	Plough	Brain
		Lathe	Unknown	3000 BC	Body	Cutting tool	Brain
		Horse and cart	Meso-potamia	2500 BC	Animal	Wheel	Brain
		Spinning wheel	India	c.1000	Body	Wheel	Brain
		Typewriter	US	1867	Body	Platen	Brain
	With controllable mach. power	Steam train	UK	1829	Steam engine	Wheel	Brain
		Car	Germany	1885	Internal combustion engine	Wheel	Brain
		Aeroplane	US	1903	Internal combustion engine	Propeller blade	Brain
	With uncontrollable mach. power	Sail boat	Egypt	3300 BC	Wind	Boat hull	Brain
		Water-mill	Greece	85 BC	Water	Grindstone	Brain
		Wind-mill	Persia	664	Wind	Grindstone	Brain
		Arkwright's water frame	UK	1769	Water	Frame mechanism	Brain
Mechanisation with automatic control	Automatic devices	Clock	Europe	c.1300	Clockwork	Mechanical hands	Machine
		Pressure cooker	France	1680	Open fire	Steam	Machine
		Steam pump	UK	1705	Steam engine	Pump	Machine
		Jacquard loom	France	1801	Steam engine	Pump	Machine
		Automatic machine tool	US	1860	Electric motor	Cutting tool	Machine
		Electronic typewriter	US	1960	Electric motor	Platen	Machine

		Device	Country	Year	Power	Action	Control
Mechanisation with automatic control	With semi-automatic control	Flour-mill	US	1785	Steam engine	Conveyor	Machine/brain
		Block-making machinery	UK	1808	Steam engine	Conveyor	Machine/brain
		Biscuit-making machinery	UK	1830	Steam engine	Conveyor	Machine/brain
		Meat packing equipment	US	1880	Electricity/steam engine	Conveyor	Machine/brain
		Assembly line	US	1913	Electricity	Conveyor	Machine/brain
	Automation	Transfer line	UK	1923	Electric motors	Cutting mechanism/conveyor	Machine with systems approach
		Computer controlled machine tool	US	1960	Electric motor	Cutting mechanism	Programmable machine
		Robot	US	c.1960	Electric motor	Mechanical hands	Programmable machine
		Robot with vision	UK	1973	Electric motor	Mechanical hands	Machine with 'feedback'

without my brain telling my fingers to thump up and down on them.

In one of the early mechanised devices, the horse and cart, an animal is responsible for power, while a person controls the contraption. But the element responsible for action – the cart's wheels and axles – is mechanical. The horse and cart is a simple example of a mechanism that saves the human body from doing something, in this case moving its legs to propel itself.

In the second kind of mechanisation, hardware is responsible for both power and action. In a car, for instance, the wheels, gears and so on provide action at the same time as the engine accounts for power. When you drive a car, a mechanism saves you the trouble both of moving your legs *and* of burning up your own supply of energy.

Wind- and water-mills are another subdivision of mechanised devices. Like cars, they use inanimate power sources, currents of air or water. But these power sources are not within a person's control. A medieval miller could not grind his corn without wind; but a modern car driver can travel in any conditions (providing his vehicle's mechanical parts are working properly).

The three remaining types of mechanised contraption are all, at least partly, automatic. In other words, they are mechanically controlled; a person does not have to be present to supervise them. Only one of the types, however, is *automated*. I'll return to the precise definition of automation later.

Simple automatic devices are far from new (see the fourth section of the Table). Soon after the first machine tools appeared late in the 18th century, engineers modified them so that they could work by themselves for at least some of the time. An operator would set his machine so that it cut, or fashioned in some other way, a piece of metal automatically. The workman would not have to do anything while the operation took place. The control devices here were camshafts and stops that ensured the machine's cutting tool moved correctly.

Going back even further, the pressure cooker was another early automatic device. It was invented in 1680 by the Frenchman Denis Papin. In the pressure cooker, a regulator automatically keeps the pressure at a specified level. The gadget has worked so well that many people's kitchens, even today, would seem a little barer without one. The clock with mechanical chimes is yet another automatic device. No one has to be around to ensure that the machine strikes the hour on cue; if they did, the contraption would be somehow self-defeating. In Salisbury Cathedral in Wiltshire you can see a clock that for 700 years has struck the hour automatically, assuming, that is, that people took the trouble to wind it up. (Which, incidentally, they did not for much of the last century, during which time the mechanism was largely forgotten and gathered dust in a storage room.)

The fifth example of mechanisation (illustrating the second kind of automatic machinery) concerns semi-automatic equipment. Here people are required for only some elements of control. In this category are the conveyor systems of the 19th and early 20th centuries with which, for instance, the Royal Navy in 1808 made pulley blocks at Portsmouth dockyard and Henry Ford's first factories assembled cars. In these systems, parts move from one part of the factory to another on an automatic conveyor. But people have to be present. They stand next to the lines to fit things onto the parts as they move past. In assembly lines in car factories, for instance, they attach wheels and so on to a moving chassis.

Finally, the Table shows the sixth kind of mechanism — truly automated devices. These are automatic contraptions, with one or more extra ingredients that concern control. To get a strict definition of automation, we can say:

AUTOMATION = MECHANISATION + AUTOMATIC CONTROL + (one or more of)
a) SYSTEMS APPROACH
b) PROGRAMM-ABILITY
c) FEEDBACK

Let us consider each of these extras in turn. With a systems approach, factories make things by passing them through successive stages of manufacturing without people intervening. So transfer lines, which made their debut in car factories in the decade before the Second World War, count as automated systems. These carry components past lines of machine tools which each cuts them automatically. People are not required; the machines clamp the parts onto themselves without a workman being present. Thus transfer lines are different from assembly lines (although the two are sometimes mixed up) where people are very much in evidence.

With 'programmability', the second of the three extras that are important in automation, a system can do more than one kind of job. An industrial robot* is an automated machine; it works automatically *and* an operator can reprogram the computer that controls it to make the machine do different things. It can be as much at home welding bits of metal together as holding a spray gun to paint a car body.

Finally, feedback makes an automatic device vary its routine according to changes that take place around it. An automatic machine tool with feedback would have sensors that detect, for instance, if the metal it is cutting is wrongly shaped. If it is, the

---

*For the moment, consider a robot to be a mechanical arm that acts similarly to a human's and is controlled by a computer. We will consider robots in depth in chapter 7.

sensors instruct the machine to vary its routine accordingly. Other examples of devices with feedback are robots with vision or other sensors that can 'see' or 'feel' what they are doing. (More of these strange contraptions later in the book.)

Engineers have unashamedly borrowed the term 'feedback' from the human body. We are chock-a-block with feedback systems. The eyes, nose, skin and ears: all are devices for receiving information, which in scientific jargon are called sensors. The body's sensors relay information from the outside world to the brain. This decides what the information means and sends new data, in the form of pulses transmitted along nerve fibres, to what scientists would call actuators. In ordinary language, these are arms, legs, feet and so on. They are devices that act. The total adds up to a feedback system. Such systems can be mirrored by mechanical assemblies. Consider, for instance, Figure 1 – which shows the human and mechanical equivalents of a mechanism that decides if a room is too dark and, on the basis of this analysis, turns on a light (or leaves it off).

Most examples of automation in factories today are not 'programmable'; neither do they work with feedback. They are simply sets of machines linked together according to 'systems' approach. These mechanisms are inflexible. They turn out only one kind of part, which is all very well if the manufacturer wants to make thousands of identical components. But if he wants to change his routine, the machinery is not very useful. Automation has yet to make much of an impact, simply because not enough people make objects in large enough volumes to take advantage of the approach.

At least, this is the case while automation is inflexible. But, and this is a big but, flexible automation is on the way. Here, automated machinery has programmability and feedback and can turn out different kinds of goods. The equipment will make a tremendous difference to factory floors throughout the world. Flexible automation adds up to a new industrial era.

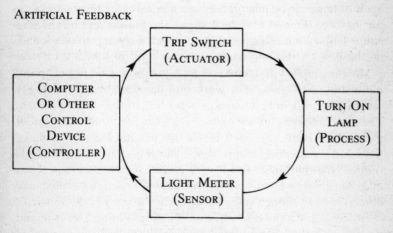

Figure 1: Human and artificial feedback

Chapter Three
Four industrial revolutions

People have labelled as 'revolutions' three episodes in the industrial history of the world, and we are now entering the fourth. In the first big change, which historians with permissible grandeur call The Industrial Revolution, people made advances in both the 'power' and 'action' elements of machinery. (I am borrowing from the classification set out in the last chapter.)

Making this great change possible was, first, the steam engine; in the early part of the 18th century, steam was harnessed to make a controllable, moveable power source. Secondly, innovators such as Richard Arkwright and James Hargreaves devised mechanical contraptions to make spinning and weaving more efficient. The first industrial revolution took place in England between 1760 and 1840.

In the second revolution, from 1880 to 1920, electricity was the technical driving force. It provided power for factories that was easier and cheaper to control than steam. The revolution's epicentre was the US. It was marked also by the growing importance of science-based industries, such as chemicals and electrical goods, and the use of scientifically-designed production methods, such as the semi-automatic assembly lines introduced in the last chapter.

The third industrial revolution coincided with the advent of automation – in its inflexible form. In this revolution, the main features were advances in the control of manufacturing processes so that things could be made more cheaply, with greater precision and (often) with fewer people. And this change, which occurred around the middle of this century, also featured a new machine that was to greatly influence the world, the electronic computer.

The US Congress's investigation into automation and unemployment in 1961 summed up: 'Automation is the third phase in the development of technology that began with the industrialisation of the 18th century. First came mechanisation, which created the factory system and separated labour and management in production. In the early 20th century, mass production . . . [became] . . . so expensive that the ownership of industry had to be divorced from management and atomised into millions of separate shareholdings. Finally, since World War II, automation has added the elements of automatic control and decision-making, turning the factory from a haphazard collection of machines into a single, integrated unit and requiring production on an enormous scale. Mechanisation was a technology based on forms and applications of power. Mass production was a technology based on principles of production and organisation. Automation is a technology based on communication and control.'

What of the fourth industrial revolution?

In this, automation will become important in many more areas of industry than hitherto. At present, only relatively few parts of industry make their products with automated systems, of the sort which turn out only single types of product. Such equipment is fine for firms that make things in large production runs – cars, for instance – or in continuous-process industries that make products such as chemicals or food in steady, unbroken streams. But the hardware is not much use to anyone else.

The fourth revolution will be characterised by automated machines that are versatile and programmable and can make different things according to different sets of computer instructions.

John Diebold, founder of the Diebold Group, a US firm of management consultants, was one of the most perceptive of the early commentators on automation. He realised as early as 1952 that the inflexible automation of that period had limited use. In his book of that year, *Automation: the Advent of the Automatic Factory*, Diebold wrote: 'Many of the automatic and partially automatic factories so widely written about depend on inflexible production machinery of the type which is adaptable only to extremely long runs of product and useless for the more common medium of short runs . . . Only when the problem of automatic production of medium and short runs is solved will automatic control mechanisms be used to fullest advantage.'

Nine years later, Diebold advised Congress's subcommittee on automation and employment: 'We have not yet really begun to feel the effect of automation in our society and it can be a lot broader than it has appeared thus far.'

In other words: 'You ain't seen nothing yet.'

Let's look at conventional inflexible automation, a car plant with a transfer line for instance. Transfer lines require virtually no workers except for loading and unloading. They contain rows of machine tools that cut and drill metal blocks as they pass from one to another. Clamps automatically keep the blocks in place in front of each machine. In this way, raw lumps of metal gradually take shape as they pass up the line; finally, they become gear-box casings, crankshafts or other parts depending on the nature of the system.

Suppose the factory's owner wants to change the type of part made with the equipment. There is one simple answer to this problem: he can't. The only way to change the part – to make a gear-box casing of a slightly different shape for instance – is to take the system apart and rebuild it from scratch.

Transfer lines cost several million pounds. Once someone owns one, he does not want to scrap it in a hurry. So the people who operate such equipment make with it only parts that they can be reasonably sure will not change in shape for at least a couple of years. Further, they can justify the immense cost of the hardware only if it works for a large proportion of the day, turning out huge quantities of identical parts.

The vast majority of factories cannot use automated systems. In an industrial country such as the US or Britain, seventy-five per cent or so of all parts are produced in small batches of a hundred or so at a time. In between the different batches, the parts are constantly varied to suit changing tastes. For instance, it is a rare electric-motor company that makes only one type of device. Far more likely, in a normal day, it will run off, say, ten motors of a certain power, a dozen with a power twice that, twenty of a different size to fit into a bigger appliance . . . and so on. The parts that go into these motors will all be of different shapes. Which explains why, to such firms, automation is not, at present, appropriate.

How does an ordinary factory make things today? It uses a

process that has changed little in outline for the past two centuries. Consider a manufacturer of, say, fuse-box casings. He first casts the rough shape of perhaps 100 boxes from molten metal. A fork-lift truck takes these to another part of the works where someone makes holes in them with a drilling machine. Another worker takes them to a store, where they probably lie for a couple of days; then they are taken to a milling machine whose operator cuts the components to make a smooth finish. There might be a few more machines later in the process, all with their own operators and people to transport the boxes.

The process is slow, inefficient, and requires lots of people, space and machinery. Of course, some bright engineer could devise for the manufacturer automated equipment that turns out the fuse-box casings in a series of steps on a transfer line. But as the factory must constantly vary its output – to cater for different customers who want different kinds of fuse-boxes, perhaps to fit into equipment of different size or power – such a system would be used for only a fraction of the working day.

There is another problem. The factory has a nice little sideline making castings for gear boxes. It needs the clumsy collection of independent machine tools to turn out these products. Take them away and replace them with a single-purpose automated line and the manufacturer would find much of his sales had dried up.

What a wonderful solution if someone could make an automated system that turns out not just one kind of product but several variations! The factory owner would then get the benefits of automation – reduced labour and machinery costs, greater speed and reliability – but on terms that suited him.

The system would be a big improvement on inflexible automation. It would be as though a conjurer had discovered how to graduate from the mundane business of producing from his sleeve a boring sequence of white tennis balls; instead, he finds he can draw out a dazzling series of balls coloured red, green, yellow and blue.

Events not far short of such bizarre conjuring tricks are starting to occur on factory floors. Flexible, automated machinery is now becoming technically feasible. Later chapters will consider the hardware in detail. Featuring in this are robots – the most interesting example of flexible automation – but other kinds of equipment enter the story as well. The new machinery will have two main effects.

First, the equipment will bring the benefits of automation to manufacturers who produce things in small batches, so reducing the size of factories and the numbers of people who work in them. Secondly, in societies where there is competition among industries, the factories that do not introduce the hardware will go to the wall as a result of economic pressure from the others, and this will have a big impact on the economies of those nations that do not make the transition to the new industrial age.

PART 2

The Legacy of the Past

Chapter Four
The age of mechanisation, 1760–1840

It is a long way to travel in time from the day of the robot-controlled factory to the dawn of the first industrial revolution. But travel back we shall, for events in England in the early 18th century marked the first significant steps on the road to automation, and, indeed, to the 'flexible' automation of today.

Industrialisation, of a sort, came to Britain during the Roman occupation. Works were set up to make textiles, metal goods and earthenware. These shut down when the Romans left and it was not until the 1300s that 'factories' were again seen in Britain. Kendal in the Lake District, for instance, became prominent in that era as a centre for making woollen goods. In 1340, according to R. Whately Cooke Taylor's *The Modern Factory System*, Flemish manufacturers set up weaving machines in Bristol. This, however, breached some kind of anti-capitalist by-law and magistrates fined the weavers for having the temerity to employ local workmen.

At the time of this minor dispute, wind-mills, those early examples of mechanisation, were well established. The first recorded English wind-mill started work in Bury St. Edmunds in 1191. And water-mills were abundant during the Middle Ages. Even by the 11th century, there were 5,624 of them in Britain, according to the Domesday Book.

But what was lacking in all these contraptions was a reliable, controllable power source. For years, people had experimented with steam to provide this. On 25th July, 1698, these ideas took written form in the shape of a patent from Thomas Savery of Totnes in Devon. The patent described how to raise water 'by the impellent force of fire'. Savery's invention was simplicity itself. The device had no moving parts except valves; it comprised a pair of cylinders into which steam from a boiler is admitted alternately.

The cylinders are connected to the water supply that the operator wishes to pump away. The condensing of the steam in each boiler creates a partial vacuum so that atmospheric pressure forces the water up first into one boiler and then the other; from the second boiler, it is later removed.

A rather more robust engine appeared in 1708 from the workshop of another Devon engineer, Thomas Newcomen of Dartmouth.

Newcomen's engine also used the forces of the atmosphere to raise water. But it had one cylinder instead of two; and a system of rods, which transferred the movement of a piston inside the cylinder to a pumping mechanism, ensured that the device worked with reasonable efficiency. Unfortunately for Newcomen, he was compelled to join forces with Savery as the latter's patent was so vaguely worded that it embraced the Dartmouth man's ideas as well. In 1710, the two installed a Newcomen engine in the Huel Vor tin mine in Cornwall. Two years later, they installed another device that, unlike the first one, actually worked. This pumped water from another mine in the Midlands, probably at Dudley Castle.

For all the interest in steam engines, they were yet to play a part in mechanising manufacturing industry. Their rôle in this area had to wait for developments later in the century in mechanical engineering, which would increase the efficiency of certain key manufacturing processes. And, indeed, the application of the steam engine to factories had to wait for the 'factory system', as used in the modern sense, to take shape.

Even as late as the 1850s, people were not familiar with the word 'factory'. For one thing, it was not clearly defined. The idea that the word meant a workshop was far from most people's minds; the early definition of 'factory' was of a trading establishment in a distant country.

The first factory in the modern sense, according to historians of the subject, started work in Derby in 1717. Powered by water wheels, the five-storey building twisted strands of silk into yarn suitable for weaving. According to Taylor's *The Modern Factory System*, the plant was the first 'where the motive power was supplied from outside, where operations of manufacture hitherto performed by human fingers were performed by inanimate machinery thus set in motion, and where the workpeople were employed exclusively for wages'.

The factory contained a total of 26,000 wheels used in the preparation of yarn; it could make 300,000 km of thread per day. Sir Thomas Lombe built and owned the factory. He took out a patent on its design in 1718; later he received £14,000 from the British Government 'as a consideration for the eminent services he has done the nation in discovering and introducing to full perfection at his own expense a work so beneficial to the kingdom'.

It was not the silk trade, however, that the factory system did the most to change. The industrial revolution had its biggest effect in cotton factories. Unlike silk, which is pulled from silk worms in continuous strands, untreated cotton is a mass of short, contorted fibres. Not only do these strands have to be twisted to make a yarn strong enough for weaving; they also have to be joined together longitudinally.

The original way of so 'spinning' cotton was to use a spindle and distaff. The latter is a stick on which the spinner holds a mass of fibres. These are drawn out in reasonable lengths onto a spindle; by whirling this, the spinner imparts a twist to the yarn to make it thick and strong. The spinning wheel, a technical advance because it did these jobs in one operation, was introduced to Europe from India during the Middle Ages.

But the spinning wheel still left problems for spinners, or rather their employers. In the mid-18th century, the technology of spinning had a long way to go in matching weaving techniques in terms of productivity. Until machines appeared to improve the output of the spinner, people in the textile business faced an impasse; the spinner was overworked and the weaver was underworked, simply because the supply from one could not match the demand from the other.

The flying shuttle, invented by John Kay in 1733, had been the technical advance that expanded weavers' output. It improved on the centuries-old method of weaving with a shuttle, a device that carries the horizontal threads of the weft through the vertical strands of the warp. With the ordinary shuttle, to weave cloth wider than the length of a person's arm, not one but two weavers are required. They have to sit side-by-side facing the loom, one to throw the shuttle to the right and then return it to the centre of the fabric, and the other to throw it to the left. With Kay's invention, however, one person could weave fabric of any width more quickly than two had managed before: he pulled a cord to send his shuttle 'flying' through the cloth to thread the weft through the warp at any distance.

The mechanical advances that ushered in the first industrial revolution concerned the technology of spinning. They did for this process what the flying shuttle did for weaving. Three machines were important.

First came the water frame, patented by Richard Arkwright in 1769. Arkwright, a Preston barber, collected the ideas of earlier inventors such as John Wyatt of Birmingham and set up a successful business in making machinery for cotton mills. The frame is a series of rollers driven by water power. The rollers draw out loose fibres of cotton in a regular, continuous line to make a fine thread, which is then attached to a rapidly revolving spindle which twists the thread into yarn.

The second invention was the spinning jenny which James Hargreaves patented in 1770, having developed it six years earlier. The device was named after Hargreaves's wife – a nice family touch.

The inventor, an illiterate textile worker from Blackburn, devised the machine after watching a spinning wheel that had fallen on its side onto the floor. The wheel was still revolving; so Hargreaves thought, why not arrange several wheels similarly so that they spin not one, but many, threads at the same time? Thus the jenny came into being; the biggest ones had up to 80 wheels all under the control of one person.

The jenny and the frame came together in the third important invention. The spinning mule, devised by Samuel Crompton in 1779, was a hybrid of the two earlier devices. With this, one person could control up to 1000 spindles, the power for the machinery being supplied by water.

These mechanical inventions – plus the general idea of putting people to work in large numbers in the new 'factory system' – became important in the Midlands and the North-West of England

28

during the 1770s and 1780s. Arkwright set up his first factory in 1771, in Crompton, Derbyshire. Modelled on Lombe's Derby silk works it employed 600 people, most of them children.

But the factory system still had a long way to go before it became dominant. The cotton industry was still mainly a domestic one, based in people's homes, where the important jobs of spinning and weaving were done. In 1788, there were 20,000 jennies in Britain, most of them in homes, and just 143 water-powered cotton mills – 41 in Lancashire, 22 in Derbyshire, 17 in Nottinghamshire and 11 in Yorkshire.

All the work in developing steam engines came to fruition for manufacturing industry when these devices left the coalmines and entered workshops. The big step forward was in 1785 when, for the first time, a steam engine powered a spinning machine, a mule in this case. The step removed at a stroke the need for industrialists to site their factories next to what previously had been their staple power supply – fast-flowing streams. Instead, with a controllable power source that could be sited virtually anywhere, industrialists could put their workshops in big towns, where there was a convenient supply of labour. The steam engine meant that the centre of the cotton industry moved northwards from the Pennine valleys of Derbyshire and south Lancashire to Manchester. Not only did Manchester have a big population, which made it easy for the first capitalists to recruit workers for their factories; the town was, furthermore, not too far away from the coalfields which supplied the new engines with fuel.

The factory system, plus mechanical advances plus steampower (plus coal) added up to the first industrial revolution. The industrialisation of the world had begun.

The engines in the cotton mills were based not on Newcomen's machines but on a modification devised by James Watt in 1769. These resembled Newcomen's devices only in the way that a Rolls Royce is related to a Model T Ford. With the Devon man's engine, the cylinder had to be cooled, then reheated, for each stroke of the device, wasting energy. Watt's engine contained a cylinder that was kept permanently hot and a condenser that was always cool. At the correct moment, the steam in the cylinder was drawn by a set of valves to the condenser, where it turned to water, so creating the vacuum to force the engine's piston to move. The result was a far more efficient engine than Newcomen's. Watt also devised a mechanism that let an engine impart rotary motion. This was much more useful, particularly in factories where there are a number of things that have to be turned, than the simple up-and-down movement of the Newcomen machine.

The application of steam power to spinning heralded the death knell to the old ways of the cotton industry. Lancashire towns became full of cotton factories, mainly for spinning. There were fifty-two cotton mills in Manchester in 1802, compared with two twenty years earlier. In 1812, Britain could boast 360 cotton mills containing 4.6 million mule spindles.

Before long, steam was applied to weaving also. The power loom was invented in 1785, by Edmund Cartwright, a clergyman-poet who held a position at Lincoln Cathedral. But technical problems prevented its use becoming widespread until 1805. In 1813, there were just 2,400 power looms in Britain. The number rose to 85,000 by 1833, and 250,000 in 1850.

As the new machines for the textile industry – woolmaking was to follow cotton in becoming mechanised – became popular, another new industry grew in importance. This was the business of making machines; with it, the class of the professional engineer started to emerge. Machinery required both the people to make it, and other machines which the new engineers used as their tools. One set of machinery fed off another, until industrial Britain was full of it.

The skills of the British engineers in the early 19th century developed from those of the blacksmiths and millwrights who fashioned the machines that entered the first factories. Advances in ironmaking and metallurgy helped these people to make Britain the world's workshop in the 1800s. Engineers such as Henry Maudslay (who in 1799 invented the modern machine tool in the shape of a screw-cutting lathe), Joseph Whitworth, Joseph Clement – all were names that were synonymous with technical skill and precision.

From such people evolved the famous builders of bridges and railways later in the century. They also played a part in laying the foundations for the automated factories of the modern era. Faced with a big shipbuilding programme, the Royal Naval Dockyards at Portsmouth decided to mechanise the production of the pulley blocks used in ships' rigging. Sir Marc Brunel, the father of the even more famous I.K. Brunel, designed the forty-five machines needed for the job, and Henry Maudslay made them.

Arranged in a row so that parts were transferred from one to another without people becoming involved, the machines constituted the precursor to the modern production line. Ten unskilled men did the work for which, previously, 110 skilled blockmakers were required; and by 1808 the machines were turning out 130,000 blocks per day.

It would be absurd to suggest that technical change alone was the reason that Britain was the first nation to industrialise. Other potent forces were at work too. The increased population of England and Wales, which rose from 6 million in 1740 to 9 million in 1801 and 18 million in 1851, expanded demand at home for manufactured products. Abroad, the opening-up of ship routes and colonisation created huge export markets for British goods, especially those containing cotton. In the middle of the 18th century, a stable political climate encouraged savings and investment which, later, went into the creation of the new factories.

By the end of the century, however, the political situation had changed. There was a costly war to fight against Napoleon abroad. And at home the authorities had to face the beginning of a popular reform movement which they went to great pains to suppress. The conditions were far from good for the orderly transition from the agrarian England of the 1750s to the industrial society of the 19th century. An anonymous writer in the late 1800s, quoted in Taylor's *The Modern Factory System*, commented:

'The foundations on which it [the industrial revolution] reposes were laid in obscurity, and its early combination developed without attracting the notice of statesman or philosopher, and the concomitant development of national wealth having been unfortunately made subservient to the wasteful necessities of war, and its results consumed, the natural consequences of the labour market were disturbed in such a way that added very materially to the difficulties of a new and untried phasis (sic) of social life.

'There thus crept into unnoticed existence a closely-condensed population, under modifying influence the least understood, to whose education, religious wants, legislative and municipal protection, no care was taken and for whose physical necessities the more forethought was requisite from the very rapidity with which men were attracted to these new industrial centres.'

E.P. Thompson spells out the position rather more roughly in *The Making of the English Working Class*:

'The people were subject simultaneously to an intensification of two intolerable forms of relationship: those of economic exploitation and of political oppression. Relations between employer and labourer were becoming both harsher and less personal . . . At each point where he [the worker] sought to resist exploitation, he was met by the forces of employer or state, and commonly of both . . . Over the period 1790–1840 there was a slight improvement in average material standards. Over the same period there was intensified exploitation, greater insecurity and increasing human misery.'

According to that prolific historian Taylor, the people who had to work with the new equipment were hardly inclined to rhapsodise about it. In *The History of the Factory System*, Taylor says: 'They [the workers] saw the labour that they had been accustomed to do with their hands, and that was intimately related to every action and passion of their lives, performed, and far better performed, by a passionless, indefatigable machine . . . Gloomily, amid tumult, fear and suffering was the modern factory system introduced.'

Often, the craft workers showed their distaste for the new hardware by smashing it. Not only did it make their lives less interesting, by actually working better than them it threatened to take away their jobs. In 1767, for instance, Richard Arkwright left Blackburn because of riots by workers demonstrating against his water frames. The year afterwards, James Hargreaves saw his home, also in Blackburn, wrecked, and several jennies destroyed.

With the advent of steam power in factories, the mood of the rioters became fiercer. One of Arkwright's steam-powered mills in Chorley was wrecked in 1796. After this, it became common to guard such installations as though they were military establish-ments. The unrest reached a peak in 1811 and 1812 in the Mid-lands. During the Luddite riots, named after the reputedly crazy Ned Ludd (a textile worker who, thirty years before, had smashed his machine to bits), 1,000 stocking frames and eighty lace machines were destroyed. If the rate at which machines suffered 'accidents' was impressive, the human accident rate in factories was alarming. This was especially so as the industrial revolution progressed. Even by Victorian times, when there were at least some laws to protect workers, 500 people died in factories every year, with some 10,000 injuries. In one month in 1895, 49 people were killed in plants, and to add to the score there were 174 amputations with 130 people suffering head injuries or fractures and four workers losing eyes.

When they were not being killed or injured, the workers had to put up with dreadful conditions.

'Often in beautiful and secluded valleys, the uncongenial struc-tures rose, and ever in naked and unredeemed ugliness. It is a most significant characteristic of the establishment of the modern factory system that it was accomplished by a complete absence of aesthetic feeling, that it seems never to have occurred to the factory master of the day that his place of work could be other than a bare, blank, brutalising edifice, devoid alike of comfort and of the faintest effort at adornment.' (*The Modern Factory System*)

During the industrial revolution, the biggest social effect of all was the move away from the countryside to the towns. In 1769, some 5.5 million of the 8.5 million people in England and Wales worked on the land. By 1851, the number of agricultural workers had dwindled to 2 million out of a population of 18 million. In 1891, the figure was 780,000 out of 26 million. From the 1850s, towns-people outnumbered rural dwellers. In 1851 there were 29 towns with populations above 50,000 whereas, 100 years earlier, there had been just two – London and Edinburgh.

The output of Britain's industry was immense. The burgeoning cotton and iron goods industries lifted the country's industrial out-put by 23 per cent in the decade to 1815. In the next few decades, the growth rate was even more impressive: 39 per cent between 1815 and 1825, and then 47, 37 and 39 per cent. These growth rates correspond to figures of 3–4 per cent per annum, far beyond what the UK economy can manage in the early 1980s. (In the 1960s, however, the Japanese economy was growing at a quicker rate than even the industrial output of 19th century Britain.) By the 1850s, the UK produced two-thirds of the world's coal, half its iron and cotton cloth, five-sevenths of its steel and two-fifths by value of its hardware.

By this time, however, Britain had reached its peak as an industrial nation. As the century progressed, other countries were to overtake it in terms of industrial strength. Britain had all but lost the pioneering spirit of the engineers and inventors in the cotton trade who had laboured to lay a firm base for the mechanisation of the late 1700s.

In the place of this spirit, the Victorian era saw a grasping desire to make easy profits through trade and commerce abroad, rather than an eagerness to innovate in industry at home. Mixed with this attitude was humbug: rather than build on the skills of the innovators of the past, the Victorians remembered them with sanctimonious ceremonies which, in reality, meant very little.

This was graphically illustrated in Bolton in 1863 when the local worthies erected a statue of Samuel Crompton, the inventor of the spinning mule, who had been born in the town. To lead the procession in the unveiling ceremony, the dignitaries hauled out of the local poorhouse the one man they could find who was a relation of the 18th century inventor. After an hour or two of glory, the man was taken back to the poorhouse and the door banged shut on him – its echo signified that the era of men like Crompton was well and truly over. With it had gone Britain's leadership in factory mechanisation.

Chapter Five
The start of mass production, 1880–1920

If Britain was the centre of the first industrial revolution, America led the way in the second. The genius for discovering more efficient ways of making things in factories passed from one side of the Atlantic to another some time during the 1800s until, by the end of that century, the US was unquestionably the world's foremost industrial power.

Just when the transition occurred is impossible to say. But the seeds of the change were sown as early as 1781. In that year, jealous of Britain's lead in textile-making machinery, Parliament passed a law prohibiting the export of such equipment. The law makers were especially anxious that Britain's former colonies in North America, which five years before had declared independence, should not acquire the know-how to make cotton goods by mechanisation, and thereby challenge the industrial superiority of the 'old country'.

But the American manufacturers were determined to find out Britain's industrial secrets. And find them out they did, thanks to the superlative memory of a young textile worker named Samuel Slater.

At the age of 14, Slater became an apprentice in the workshop of Jedediah Strutt, one of the foremost machinery makers of the day. In terms of engineering skills, Strutt's works had a similar status to today's Bell Laboratories or Rolls-Royce's Derby workshops. They were humming with outstanding technical innovation, and aspiring young engineers from all over the country were attracted to work there. Slater worked with Strutt for seven years, learning a lot about the machinery industry. Then on 13th September 1789, he sailed from London to New York, taking his knowledge with him. There he was met by representatives of the US's fledgling textile industry, who quickly put Slater's know-how to use in a string of new factories.

The first mill built to the new principles, powered by water and with seventy-two spindles, started up in Pawtucket, Rhode Island, in 1790. The American factory age had begun.

By 1809, there were eighty-seven cotton factories in the US, employing 80,000 spindles. In 1812, the US's first steam-powered loom went to work, six years after the corresponding machine in Britain.

Ironically, another English émigré was indirectly responsible for much of the work in the US in steam engines. In the 1790s, Josiah Hornblower, a Cornish engineer whose father had been a friend of Thomas Newcomen, took a Newcomen engine to the United States to install for a customer -- and never returned. Instead he formed an engineering business which spread the word to his adopted country about the new developments in steam.

The US was never as prominent as Britain in the business of making cotton goods. Although cotton mills in America numbered 801 in 1830 and, a decade later 1,240, by 1880, the US was turning out 300,000 tons of cotton cloth per year, roughly half as much as Britain. It was in engineering and metal-goods industries that the former colonies exploited advances in mechanisation to the full. So much so, in fact, that in 1855, Parliament despatched a Committee of Inquiry to America to investigate just how the US made its goods so well. The teacher was now ready to be taught.

The US factories gained their superiority by exploiting to the full the principle that the first English industrialists had employed, division of labour. The principle states how to reduce the cost of making a series of goods that result from a complex manufacturing operation. In the old craft-based system, a worker is responsible for a complete product; he does all the small jobs that constitute the whole manufacturing operation, before going on to start the next product. Under the new system, each employee is given just one task, a small segment of the complete operation. He repeats this task continuously on a series of semi-finished products that are passed to him from another worker, who has another job which, again, he repeats over and over. By arranging in a factory a sequence of employees, all with their own carefully-defined jobs, and who each pass on the product to the next worker in the line, industrialists found that they could make goods more quickly and cheaply than with the old system.

The principle was explained to the general population in books such as Elisha Noyce's *The Boy's Handy Book of the Manufactures and Industries of the World*. Noyce was particularly impressed with the manufacture of needles, which, he said, is 'one of those arts in which manual dexterity is acquired by minute subdivision of labour, each artisan performing only a small part of the process, but so often that the most wonderful rapidity and accuracy are obtained inasmuch that, although each needle has to pass through nearly 150 hands (together with expensive machinery) before finishing, yet they are sold at such an astonishing low price that papers containing 25 may be purchased for one penny!'

American manufacturers allied with this principle the technique of making things with interchangeable parts. This standardised components so that components of one product, a spinning machine for instance, could be interchanged with the equivalent parts of a similar device. The principle sounds absurdly straightforward today, accustomed as we are to the impeccably logical way in which manufactured goods are made out of bundles of standard parts fitted together. But the notion was not at all obvious to someone living in the 18th century. To him, major mechanisms such as grinding machines and wagons, and even the parts that went into them, were unique. There was no question of swapping parts from, say, one horse-drawn wagon to another. If a wheel in such a contraption became buckled, our forefathers could not go along to a shop and replace the damaged item with a similar part that they knew would fit. Instead, they had to get a new wheel specially made to fit their wagon.

With interchangeable parts, repair became easier. To replace defective parts, people could fit new components that had come straight from a factory. This was instead of throwing the whole contraption away, or paying someone to fashion a new component that was unique to the device under repair.

Even more importantly, the concept greatly increased the efficiency of making things in factories. Consider the options open to a manufacturer of, for instance, firearms. Each manufactured item contains dozens, if not hundreds, of parts that have to be fitted together by an assembly worker. Under the old, craft-based technique, the items are made in a hit-and-miss manner by machining, or casting, one component at a time. Then the assembly worker uses his skills to fit the bits together. Due to the inaccurate way in which the items are made, parts with the same function for different guns are different. For instance, the gun barrels for otherwise identical weapons probably vary: some might be shorter than average, some might have rough bits of casting left on them, and so on. The assembly worker has to spend considerable time and effort taking account of the varied nature of the products in order to do his job of fitting them together.

This kind of operation is perfectly satisfactory when the number of guns made per week is fairly small, say a few dozen. The manufacturer is under no great pressure to produce a lot of goods rapidly. He does not mind paying his skilled assembly worker to spend a long time making each weapon. But if demand for his products increases, his job has to speed up.

Rather than hire more highly-skilled people to do the assembly jobs, a new option became available for the industrialist of the 19th century. He could buy new, highly-accurate machines that turned out streams of identical parts for different weapons. Parts of equivalent function are interchangeable between all the guns coming out of the factory. The manufacturer finds that, although the machinery is expensive, it pays for itself as long as demand for his products continues to be high. So he attempts to keep it this way through price-cutting, advertising, 'special offers' and so on.

This style of making things is familiar to anyone who has heard of the term 'mass production'. The first mass-production industry was the firearms business in the US in the early part of the 19th century. Samuel Morse, Eli Whitney, Simeon North and the others involved in this industry set the pattern for the manufacturing techniques that are so entrenched today.

The inventive Yankees soon discovered that other products besides guns could be made with the new manufacturing methods.

Among the goods made in this way were machine tools, boots and shoes, musical instruments, watches, clocks, typewriters and sewing machines. Between 1810 and 1860, the US's annual industrial output expanded tenfold, from $200 million to $2,000 million. In 1882, it was calculated that each of the country's 3 million industrial workers produced fifty times as much per year as their counterparts half a century before, under the old craft-based manufacturing system. Such was the effect of the interchangeable parts method, allied with division of labour.

In the 1880s, the US overtook Britain as the world's leading steel supplier – then, as now, a symbol of industrial strength. Two decades or so later, the US's factories were responsible for roughly one third of the world's manufactured goods.

America's continued advances as the 20th century unfolded were due to two main technical factors. The first was the evolution of the interchangeable-parts method into the first semi-automated production techniques, in the sense that Chapter Two defined this term. The production line became a familiar sight. It is a series of machines each of which does a certain job on a product as it passes from one to another, probably on a conveyor belt or through some other transport mechanism. These lines are natural extensions of earlier advances in manufacturing; machines, however, instead of people, are used to do most of the work.

We saw in the last chapter that one forerunner of the modern production line was the series of machines for making pulley-blocks built by the Royal Navy in Portsmouth in 1808. An even earlier example was a flour mill constructed by the American inventor Oliver Evans in 1784. The plan for this would have looked like a Heath Robinson drawing. The mill processed flour with an ingenious combination of buckets, conveyors, wheels and pulleys. Virtually no person was involved.

Nineteenth-century America first took production-line techniques seriously in what might seem a strange place: the Chicago meat-packing yards. Carcasses of pigs and other animals were transferred between various machines that cut them up and hauled the meat to collecting stations. A couple of decades later, in 1913, Henry Ford brought the production line to more familiar territory, car factories. A car chassis was hauled around a factory floor, past rows of massed workers, with a conveyor system. Each worker was given the job of fixing on a particular part – a wheel, a mudguard, some nuts and bolts for the engine and so on. With this technique, Ford found that he could assemble a car body in ninety minutes compared with the twelve hours that was needed with the old 'stationary' method; in this, the chassis stayed in a fixed position and ranks of workers clustered around it, connecting components.

Ford's methods, which made the car industry into a mass-production business almost as soon as it had taken shape, are set out more fully in his book *My Life and Work*. In this, Ford explains: 'In the chassis assembly are 45 separate operations or stations. The first men fasten four mudguard brackets to the chassis frame; the motor arrives on the 10th operation, and so on in detail. Some men do only one or two small operations; others do more. The man who places a part does not fasten it – this may not be fully in place until after several operations later. The man who puts on a bolt does not put on the nut; the man who puts on a nut does not fasten it . . .'

The assembly lines in Ford's factories were *semi-automated*, according to the definition set out in Chapter 2. They required people for key parts of the operation; it was they, not inanimate machines, who had to stand by the line and fix bits onto the car chassis as it trundled past.

About the same time as production lines appeared in car factories, mass-production companies took on board 'scientific management', a concept dreamed up by Frederick Taylor. Under this discipline, 'time and motion' men analysed job details in the new semi-automated and automated factories. They calculated the optimum amount of work for each labourer that would maximise the efficiency of the complete operation. In US industry, managers would have portraits of Frederick Taylor on their office walls in the same way as, half a century later, teenagers kept pictures of pop stars.

The second technical development which affected the positions of the leading industrial nations from 1860 or so onwards, concerned the increasingly important role of science and technology.

This helped increasingly to determine both *how* goods and *which* goods were made.

Thus science and technology made possible new production techniques, chiefly those which cashed in on the new power sources, gas and electricity. These forms of power constituted an advance on steam, thought, just a century before, to be such a world-beating way of driving machines. Electricity and gas-driven engines were far less bulky than their steam equivalents; and, most importantly, the power that they required for their action could be 'piped' to the most inaccessible place just like running water. At the same time as the new power sources were gaining a foothold, the new products that science and technology made possible started entering the market place. The petrol-driven car, chemicals and electrical goods – these were the products on which the world's most dynamic countries began to base their economies. Once again, it was the US that led the way in the speed with which it adjusted.

After attaining, in 1850, the position of the world's foremost industrial power, how did Britain let the lead slip away? It was not just the US that was quicker to adapt to the new ideas in industry; the same could be said of France, Germany and other European nations.

There are three loosely-related reasons for the decline. First, Britain made little intellectual effort to get to grips with the new science-based industries and the technically-advanced production methods with which other countries were experimenting. This reluctance showed up in the low value given to the teaching of science in schools. In particular, schools and colleges paid little attention to applied science and technology that could be of use to industry.

As early as 1830, Charles Babbage pointed out in *Reflections on the Decline of Science in England and on Some of its Causes*, 'It cannot have escaped the attention of those ... who have had opportunities of examining the state of science in other countries that in England, particularly with respect to the more difficult and abstract sciences, we are much below other nations not merely of equal rank, but below several even of inferior power.'

Five years later, in his own peculiarly roundabout way, Babbage, in his *The Economy of Machinery and Manufacturers*, called for a coming together of the disciplines of science and manufacturing.

'It has been shown that the division of labour is no less applicable to mental production than to those in which material bodies are concerned; and it follows that the efforts for the improvement of its manufactures, which any country can make with the greatest probability of success, must arise from the combined exertions of all those most skilled in the theory, as well as the practice, of the arts.'

L.T.C. Rolt, in *Victorian Engineering*, gives a 20th century view of Britain's deficiencies: 'Although the Victorian educational system may have produced great Empire builders, soldiers and administrators, it failed to produce great engineers. Because, in the minds of gentlemen, business professionalism was tainted with "trade", the system produced amateurs . . . High principles and gentlemanly conduct rated higher than intellectual ability.'

The second factor that held Britain back in the new science-based industries was the lack of status given to those engineers that the educational system did produce who, according to some commentators, could have steered the country in the right direction. In his book just quoted, Rolt mourns the death, within a few months of each other in 1859 and 1860, of Isambard Kingdom Brunel, Robert Stephenson and Joseph Locke, and comments sadly on the crowds who thronged to Stephenson's funeral: 'Never again would a British engineer command so much esteem and affection; never again would the profession stand so high. To some extent, it was inevitable, for as knowledge rapidly accumulated, so the profession ramified. Increasingly, teams of more or less anonymous experts became responsible for new developments rather than a single brilliant individual . . . No longer bestriding his profession with such easy assurance, he [the engineer] became the servant instead of the master of the boardroom and the accountant.'

Finally, Britain's economic circumstances saw to it that there was little incentive to invest in the new industries. The merchants and traders who had most of the country's money were, quite simply, preoccupied with putting it where they could make quick profits, which often meant overseas, in Britain's colonies, rather than in

42

building up new industries at home. In a masterly summing-up of Britain's fall as an industrial power in Chapter 9 of *Industry and Empire*, E.H. Hobsbawm points out that in 1870, Britain's investments abroad began to exceed capital formation at home. Meanwhile, domestic industry was content to produce old-fashioned goods, made with obsolescent technologies, to sell to the captive markets of the overseas colonies.

Hobsbawm goes on: 'The British economy as a whole tended to retreat from industry into trade and finance, where our services reinforced our actual and future competitors, but made very satisfactory profits ... Britain, we may say, was becoming a parasitic rather than a competitive economy, living off the remains of world monopoly, the underdeveloped world, her past accumulations of wealth and the advance of her rivals.'

Thus Britain stumbled into the 20th century, whereas – economically at any rate – it had strode energetically into the 19th. Abroad, the country's industrial rivals continued to pay more attention to the training of engineers as a way of keeping their technology-based firms successful. That many of the engineers who founded and operated successful businesses abroad were British – the growth of soccer in Europe resulted from émigré British engineers starting factory football teams – was no cause for consolation. Rather, this fact should have sounded a warning. The Victorians chose to ignore it.

In the Second World War, British technology had a brief renaissance. The special circumstance of wartime gave engineers a free hand to make some impressive advances, in the area of radar, communications and electronic code-breaking; and these feats of technology did much to help the country win the day. After hostilities stopped, the country soon reverted to its pre-war stance and engineers returned once more to the shadows of national life. There was one technical area, however, in which British expertise was important. Although the country failed to cash in very much on this field of development, it played a big part in developing a machine that was soon to have an enormous impact in the technology of making things – the electronic computer.

Chapter Six
Enter the computer, 1940–1980

The age of automation did not get under way properly, at least not in the public's mind, until the 1950s. For one thing, the word itself became common only about this time. Secondly, the world was then getting accustomed to a machine that would greatly facilitate the automation process, the electronic computer.

Automated factories do not necessarily contain computers. Remember the definition of automation from Chapter 2. The term describes any way of automatic working (one in which machines are responsible for control so that the mechanism is 'self-acting') with one of three extra control factors. One of these 'optional extras' is a 'systems' approach, in which a series of mechanisms are meshed together to do several manufacturing operations without people being involved; the other two factors are programmability and feedback.

The first automated factories, according to this definition, were the ones containing transfer lines that appeared in the 1930s. A transfer line is a series of machines each of which receives parts in turn and does a particular operation, for instance cutting, drilling or stacking things on top of each other. Each machine in the line receives parts from a conveyor which moves according to a set program of instructions; the machine 'grabs' its part with special grippers and then does its job largely independently of people.

The transfer line was a British invention. The first one started work at the Coventry factory of Morris Motors in 1923. It comprised fifty-three machining stations that did jobs such as tapping, drilling and boring on parts as they moved up the line from one station to the next. The system did need some people; for example they had to lift raw parts onto the system and take finished ones off it.

With the system, six men could make fifty-three cylinder blocks for Morris cars in one hour. With conventional machining methods, in which the work was done by individual machines each with its own operator, the rate of progress was sixteen blocks per hour. And this required not six, but thirty-six workmen.

Morris Motors's transfer line did not contain an electronic computer. Nor did the similar lines that quickly became important in the car factories of the 1930s. This would have been impossible as the electronic computer was invented only in 1945.

When it did arrive, the computer made its entry onto the world's stage with hesitant, ungainly steps. For many years, the power of the machines was limited by their cost, huge size and unreliability. And if the designers of the first computers were feeling their way, the first users were also. People simply had very little idea about how to harness these strange new devices effectively.

Nonetheless, the computer helped greatly in the process of controlling the different operations of factories, that is in linking these operations to give the 'systems approach' which, we have seen, is one of the hallmarks of automation. Before the computer, the constituent machines of a factory – for cutting, processing, assembly, handling, inspection and so on – worked away independently. Picture a football team with eleven talented individuals, each playing competently enough but with little overall direction. Add a coordinator – a 'midfield general' in the jargon of the soccer field – and the team's play, and its results, will probably improve enormously. Now translate the picture to a factory floor; add a coordinating machine to the array of previously relatively purposeless devices and you have a recipe for improved efficiency.

The automation of the 1950s and 1960s was essentially inflexible. Linked systems of machines, whether controlled by computers or not, generally turned out only one kind of product. The most important characteristic of computers – that they can be made to do different things by feeding them with different sets of instructions or programs – was scarcely appreciated. In the early days of computers, people had enough problems getting the machines to work with one set of operating rules. They had little enthusiasm for finding out how to cash in on the potential versatility of the new gadgets.

The age of inflexible automation was marked by three key

characteristics, as *Automation*, a 1956 booklet from Britain's Department of Scientific and Industrial Research, pointed out. First was 'the expansion of the scope of mechanisation by transfer devices'. The second factor was 'the rapid development of techniques of automatic control over manufacturing processes and their application to an ever-widening range of industries'; third was 'the rapid and automatic processing of an increasing range of technical and business information by the electronic digital computer'.

The document showed how the computer could do the vital job of linking up the otherwise separate operations of a factory, as in Figure 2, reprinted from the booklet.

'All operations in this imaginary factory are centrally regulated by a master production controller under the direction of the management', the booklet said.

'A computer, which forms part of the control unit, analyses information about sales, orders and changes in the market and this information combined with policy information provided by the management, gives the basis of each plan for production . . . The master production-controller releases material from the stores as it is needed and keeps an optimum load on the automatic machine tools in each line. Similarly, it releases the finished components at appropriate intervals to the assembly line, where they are automatically put together and packed for despatch. The machinery in each process – machining, inspection and packing – is regulated by subsidiary controllers, and each controller is directly linked with the master, which conveys information to it as a basis for adjustments – for instance, information about the quality of the product as a basis for regulating the settings of machines and other plant.'

The anonymous civil servant who penned the document pointed out that: 'Even in this fully automatic factory, manpower is still necessary to mind and maintain machines, to do some of the clerical work and to perform the many functions of management. But the traditional teams of operative labour, directly engaged on the process, have disappeared.'

As it turned out, the booklet's description of how computers, and other technical advances, were to change life in the factory was to be realised rather more slowly than its author thought. After all the

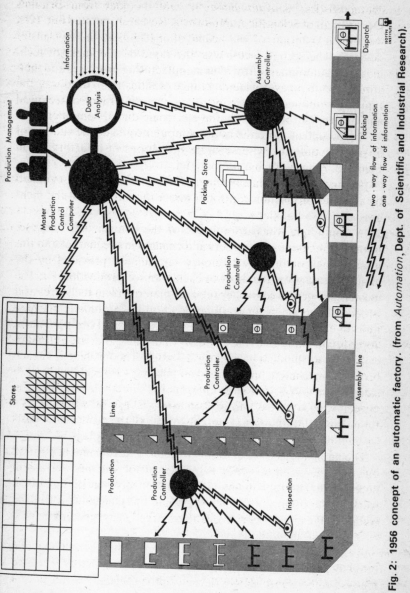

Fig. 2: 1956 concept of an automatic factory. (from *Automation*, Dept. of Scientific and Industrial Research).

talk about 'automatic factories', by the late 1960s only a few had appeared. The delay was largely due to the slow pace of development of the computer, the machine that people in the immediate post-war years pointed out could revolutionise manufacturing.

The first electronic computers appeared during the Second World War. Most technical books state that the world's first was the ENIAC, built at the University of Pennsylvania in 1945. The machine was constructed to help in the war effort. Engineers wanted it to work out the trajectories of bombs and missiles for instance. Britain played a big role in the development of the early computers. The Colossus machines, constructed at the government's secret wartime technical centre at Bletchley Park, Buckinghamshire, may well have rivalled the US machine for the accolade of the world's first electronic computer. There is a doubt, however, over whether they were 'general purpose' machines – their only role that we know anything about was to break enemy codes. We can have no doubt, however, that the technical advances at Bletchley infiltrated after the war to other places such as the National Physical Laboratory in Teddington, Middlesex, and Manchester University, and so helped the UK get off to a flying start in the brave new world of computers. Britain was responsible for the first computer with a stored program of instructions, built at Manchester University in 1948, and for the first computer built for sale, which Ferranti delivered in 1951.

A computer is a universal, automatic calculating machine. It is universal in that it can do any problem that can be presented in a program, or series of instructions written in a special computer code, which the machine's user has to prepare. The computer is automatic in that it does its work in a series of steps without anyone intervening. The term 'calculating machine', by the way, means not only that a computer can do arithmetical problems such as adding numbers, solving equations or (in a factory operation) comparing a set of data from one machine with a corresponding set from another. Also, the computer can process ordinary words, by representing text as numbers and then performing specified operations on these numbers. What can a computer do with words? It can memorise them, transmit them along telephone wires or via radio waves, search for them in computerised 'libraries', even translate them into other languages. As this is not a book about computers, I suggest you read one of the computer books listed in the appendix if you wish to learn more about how these machines work.

A universal, automatic machine of this type was first conceived by the English professor, Charles Babbage, in 1832. He specified the design for what he called an analytical engine, which, in many ways, was a forerunner of the modern computer.

Unfortunately, Babbage's engine was never built. Contemporary workmen were unable to make parts to the precision that Babbage required. There was a further point: 19th century Britain was not exactly bowled over by the prospects for the new machine. So people did not rush forward with money to help Babbage construct his strange new device. As Chapter 5 pointed out, Babbage was a critic of the scientific establishment in the mid 1800s: he certainly got little support from his scientific peers for his ideas. Like many inventors, he was years ahead of his time.

Babbage's analytical engine contained (or would have contained, had it been built) a store which holds numbers for arithmetical operations such as addition and multiplication; an arithmetic unit which does these operations; and a control unit which tells the arithmetic unit which operations the user wants carried out. It was in the control unit that Babbage came up with something revolutionary. This item gave the engine its 'universal' label. It was a system of punched cards that could be varied depending on whether the user wanted, for instance, to solve an equation or add a string of numbers. The punched cards constituted the world's first computer program. Babbage's device also contained an input unit by which numbers were fed to the machine and an output unit for getting out answers.

Structurally, today's computers are not far removed from Babbage's model. There are two major differences. First, today's computers work not on decimal digits – the numbers 0 to 9 – but on binary digits. Computers' language consists solely of strings of 0s and 1s, which can be made to represent either decimal numbers, words from the English (or any other) language or symbols of specific use to computer operators.

Secondly, today's machines are electronic while Babbage's – like all similar calculating machines before the ENIAC – was mechanical. Electronic machines do their work by sending streams of electrons along wires and through valves or pieces of semiconductor. So they are much faster than their mechanical counterparts, which rely on cumbersome wheels, gears, rods and so on.

Why were the newly invented electronic computers useful in the factories of the 1950s? We have already mentioned the role of the computer as a 'controller'. Here the machine takes note of perhaps dozens of different operations which send it data represented as sequences of binary digits. By analysing the data, the computer can, for instance, decide that the temperature at which chemicals are reacting is too high, that a sequence of machine tools is turning out items at a rate lower than envisaged or that a store of metal parts in a warehouse is about to run out because demand from the assembly line is higher than expected. The computer would then instruct an operator accordingly so that he can do something about the situation.

There are other control activities where the computer supervises not a sequence of operations, but a single machine. For instance, in the 1950s and 1960s, paper tape, produced with computers, controlled individual machine tools that cut, drilled or, in other ways, fashioned bits of metal. Machines that operated in this way were called numerically-controlled (NC) machine tools. Ferranti, at its Edinburgh research laboratories, started work on the concept in 1950 and found that numerically-controlled tools could reduce production time by a factor of 50 to 1,000, compared with the same jobs done on orthodox machine tools. At about the same time, in the US, the Massachusetts Institute of Technology demonstrated similar ideas.

In an NC machine, the computer tape does the job of an operator who, in a conventional manually-controlled tool, has to be on hand continuously to tell the machine to move in the right way to make a particular part. The operator now has only to mind the machine to ensure that it does not go wrong; the most demanding task is given to the programmer, who, with a computer's help, prepares the tape.

Mechanical 'feedback' was evident in some of the new control systems. For instance, a computer monitoring the temperature of a reaction might keep it constant by triggering an actuator – a heating coil or a valve for instance – whenever the reading fluctuated from a certain figure. Such systems were therefore 'automated', according to the definition sketched out in Chapter 2.

In process industries, in which batches of chemicals are brought together and made to react (such industries span anything from refining petroleum to making chocolate) there was also some element of programmability. Thus operators of these processes could tell their computer-controllers to make different brands of chocolate, for instance; the controller would see to it that the reaction vessel received different mixtures of cocoa or milk, or that the constituents were kept at different temperatures and pressures.

But, outside these industries, there were few opportunities for making different kinds of product with an automated system. Automation was definitely 'inflexible'. In engineering industries – which embrace activities in which parts, normally metal or plastic, are bashed, cut, shaped or assembled – programmable automation was rarely seen. There were two main reasons. First, many parts of the manufacturing process – handling, assembly and inspection of finished goods – could only rarely be mechanised, let alone automated. The technical difficulties were too great, so the manufacturing methods still largely required people. Secondly, people were still experimenting with computers and they only gradually made their way into factories.

A few figures show how slow was the pace of progress. In 1957, when the word 'automation' was on the lips of many people who believed it would bring large-scale unemployment, there were 1800 computers in the US and a mere 140 in western Europe. By 1961, the figure for the US climbed to 7,400, and western Europe contained 1,545 of the machines. In 1963, there were all of 300 computers in the UK. Compare these figures with the 700,000 big mainframes and minicomputers that the world contained in 1979, together with the millions of small microprocessor-based systems.

Research by P.C. Millson of IBM, which he presented at a conference in Harrogate, Yorkshire in 1961 on the social and economic effects of automation, shows just how little experience industry had of computers – even by this relatively late date. Millson pointed out that factory automation had progressed furthest in large-scale processing, for instance in petroleum works and the steel industry. In this kind of automation, a computer receives information from an array of instruments, analyses it and, rather than control the process directly, presents conclusions for humans to act upon. Millson also mentioned the two other main forms of automation of the period – inflexible transfer lines used in car factories and tape-controlled machine tools.

The 1960s saw computerisation start to take off – certainly as far as industry was concerned. In *Automation: Industrialisation comes of Age*, William Francois pointed out that in the US in 1955, only five firms sold automation systems for industry. In 1964, the figure was seven hundred. In 1961, a watershed was reached for the process industries. IBM announced a control system that scanned up to three hundred instruments at regular intervals to give instructions to an operator about how to modify chemical processes. Later, IBM announced a 'closed loop' system that made the adjustments automatically without requiring a human operator.

General Electric and Monsanto were among the big American companies that took advantage of computer control to automate steel mills and chemical works. In the engineering industry, many commentators wrote about a shell-making plant in Rockford, Illinois that turned out munitions from molten steel via a series of 15 automated processes with only a few workers. Use of numerical control advanced; even so, by 1962, General Electric estimated that there were only 1800 NC machine tools when the total number of machine tools in the US must have run to hundreds of thousands.

In the 1950s the USSR decided that automation could be a vital tool in pushing its industries ahead of those in the West, without the exploitation of workers which the country associated with the capitalist system. An automated factory was, for the Soviets, a symbol of the triumph of engineering skill over the adversity of the natural world.

Describing a piston factory near Moscow in his 1955 book *A Soviet Automatic Plant*, the Soviet writer A. Erivansky commented: 'The automatic factory brings the future within arm's reach. Here you can see a close likeness of what work will become in the plants and factories of the communist tomorrow.' He informed his readers: 'When you see the Soviet automatic factory, the first of its kind in the world, in action, you experience a feeling of great joy.'

There was a moral to the tale of engineering achievement, analogous to the idea in the West that automation will make a country strong and in a better position to compete in capitalist markets. The Soviet version of the story, however, stressed the personal benefits of shorter hours due to advanced technology. Erivansky pointed out that automation 'will give the workers of the Land of the Soviets unlimited opportunities for all-round development of their capabilities, and enable them to make the utmost use of all that modern culture has to offer.'

Writers in the West got excited about automation too. Eugene Grabbe in *Automation in Business and Industry* (1957) was typical. 'It is commonplace these days to hear that we are entering a second industrial revolution, the era of automation. This time it is not man's muscles that are to be replaced and extended, but rather man's brains. More specifically, what is meant is that, in business and industry, the functions accomplished by people are going to be accomplished more and more by complete networks of complex automation systems.'

People were worried, as they had been for centuries, that machines would take over their jobs. But Paul Einzig, in his *Towards the Automatic Factory: the Economic Consequences of Automation*, published in 1956, pointed out: 'Automation is bound to proceed sooner or later whether we like it or not. Our choice does not rest between automation and full employment, but between prompt automation with the possibility of moderate temporary unemployment, and delayed automation with the certainty of grave perennial unemployment until our progress has caught up with that of our competitors.'

For all the discussion about automation, in the 1950s and 1960s it failed to threaten many people's jobs. For one thing, the world's economy was expanding. Productivity increases made possible by computers resulted in increased output, not lost jobs. Secondly the big changes in computers, brought about by greater experience in their use and by their greatly reduced cost and increased power due to technical change, had yet to occur. The introduction of the integrated circuit in the early 1960s, and of the microprocessor in 1971, made computers cheaper than anyone in the 1950s could have imagined. Where once computers comprised miles of tangled wire and clumsy vacuum valves, they were now arrays of integrated circuits built out of pieces of silicon. They were far less costly, more powerful and less likely to go wrong.

The change opened up new vistas in industrial automation. People saw uses for computers, as agents of control on the factory floor, that hitherto they always thought would be too costly.

In 1963 the American Society of Tool and Manufacturing Engineers summed up the effects of technical change in a book called *Numerical Control in Engineering*. To do a series of computing steps for an engineering operation on a desk calculator would take, the society said, 1,000 hours and cost $10,000. On a medium sized computer, the same operation would cost $10 and take six minutes. With one of the new solid-state computers, the sequence of operations would take a matter of microseconds and cost fifty cents. Since then, further advances in computers (about which there are plenty of contemporary books that will supply you with the relevant statistics) have brought the time and cost factors down even more.

On top of the reduced cost and greater power of computers, there were two further advances. First engineers became expert at linking groups of computerised machines to form automated systems that were fully programmable, that is could turn out different types of product in engineering or metal-based industries. People simply became more acquainted with computers and got better at devising the programs to run them, and to let them 'talk' to each other in a meaningful way.

Secondly, the industrial robot arrived on the scene. The industrial robot is the most significant manifestation of 'flexible automation'. It turned out most useful in the kinds of jobs in engineering that hitherto could not be automated – inspection, handling things, spraying paint and putting objects together.

The robot age, however, hardly burst on the world overnight. Its gestation stretched back several centuries; and its progenitors were not engineers and technicians – rather they were storytellers and showmen.

PART 3

The Robot Age

Chapter Seven
Anatomy of a robot

What is a robot? People have been arguing about the definition for much of this century. The confusion has badly harmed the image of the machines, at least in Britain. Quite simply, the word 'robot' frightens many people. As a result, many manufacturers fear their workers won't like the devices and are more than a little scared of employing the equipment in their factories.

A lot of people think of robots as machines that both do the work of humans and look like them. Strictly speaking, these devices should be termed androids, from the Greek 'andros' meaning of man and 'eidos' meaning form. A number of androids have indeed been created; but they have been mostly for amusement value. Very few of them have done any serious work. In an industrial sense (at the moment anyway) the android is a non-starter.

Then we come to machines such as traffic lights or even clocks which some people, perhaps in flights of fancy, have labelled robots. Such definitions sometimes crop up in books written for children, presumably because the authors think that, by giving commonplace objects exciting names, the books will somehow be more appealing. This shallow thinking is to be deplored. It means whole generations of children might grow up with the wrong idea of what a real robot entails. The true name for gadgets such as clocks and traffic lights, if an all-encompassing label is required, is an 'automaton'. This word is derived from the Greek 'automatos', which describes something that acts by itself. Of course, from this comes 'automation' – a word much discussed in earlier chapters. By no stretch of the imagination may we describe as 'robots' the myriad examples of automation mentioned already.

So how should we define a robot? A good description is provided in Jasia Reichardt's valuable *Robots: Facts, Fiction and Prediction*. A robot is a machine 'which wholly or in part imitates man –

sometimes in appearance and sometimes in action'. Thus a gadget which simulates, say, the action of a person's limb can be called a robot. Likewise a machine that walks up and down and gives a passable impression of smoking a cigarette can also be bracketed in this category.

As we shall see in more detail in a moment, there is nothing new about efforts to make machines that correspond with this definition. They have been going on for centuries. But for many years, the aspiring robot-builders set their sights too high. They attempted to make androids. These machines were simply too ambitious, however; they were good amusement value but they would never have done anything useful.

The turning point came in the 1950s. Engineers in the US decided they would be rather more pragmatic and make 'robots' that merely imitate the *actions* of people. The devices would not necessarily look like humans at all. The most useful part of a person – from the point of view of doing physical work – is his or her arms. So the engineers decided to build mechanical arms that worked in a similar way to people's; they were articulated about several points to include the mechanical equivalents of elbows, shoulders and wrists.

Any piece of mechanical engineering has to be controlled in some way. It was fortunate for these pioneering engineers that, about the time they designed the new robots, there came into widespread existence an extremely useful machine for controlling things – the electronic computer. A computer, which operates according to a set of programs that can be changed easily, is a highly flexible device. So a mechanical arm that is linked to a computer can operate in a varied way depending on the software that the latter contains.

The obvious analogy is with the brain. The brain can command a person's limbs to do an infinite number of activities – anything from kicking a football to punching someone in the face. That is to say it may be 'programmed' in an infinite number of ways. Likewise, industrial robots – mechanical arms linked to computers – can operate in many varied ways in factories. They can, for instance, simulate the action of a human arm in painting a car body; they can take lumps of metal out of casting machines; or they can lift heavy sacks and put them in containers. The industrial robot is to play a big part in the era of flexible automation mentioned in earlier chapters.

In November 1979, the years of confusion about how to define robots came to an end, at least for those interested in the industrial variety of the machines. The Robot Institute of America made this grand statement: 'A robot is a programmable, multifunctional manipulator designed to move material, parts, tools or specialised devices through variable programmed motions for the performance of a variety of tasks.'

If you write to the institute – it is based in Detroit – you can receive a little card with this message printed on it, just to remind you that the issue of what constitutes a robot is cleared up forever.

But what about the robot of science fiction? This is a quite different animal, looking and talking like a person and, often, surpassing a human being in some qualities, being resistant to bullets for instance. For the student of the robot in science fiction, all roads lead back to *R.U.R.* or *Rossum's Universal Robots*, the famous play that introduced the word into the English language. *R.U.R.* was written in 1920 by the Czech playwright Karel Capek and translated into English three years later. The play was first performed in the National Theatre in Prague on 25 January 1921.

In *R.U.R.* a factory run by a man called Rossum turns out android machines which have a wonderful capacity for work. At first, the products sell extremely well to other manufacturers and Rossum, presumably, is making a packet. But, later, matters take a turn for the worse: the robots become progressively more advanced and even learn to think for themselves. Eventually, they rise up and overcome their human masters.

Fabry, one of the characters in the play, spells out the usefulness of the robots. (This is at a time when the human beings in the story are still wondering at the capabilities of the machines rather than being terrified of them.) His words strike a chord among many factory workers who today fear they will suffer from automation: 'One Robot can replace two and a half workmen. The human machine . . . was terribly imperfect. It had to be removed sooner or later . . . It was not very effective.'

Capek coined the word robot from the Czech 'robota' meaning servitude. After the machines in his play have discovered servitude is not to their taste and kill most of their former masters, Radius, the chief robot, sums up the position with these stirring words: 'The power of man has fallen. By gaining possession of the factory, we have become masters of everything. The power of man has fallen. A new world has risen. The rule of the Robot.'

It is worth quoting some more from Radius, not so much because of the excellence of his speeches (possibly the words sounded better in the original Czech) but because the lines are the forerunners of so many that have appeared in science fiction over the years, scaring people stiff of anything called a robot. 'The world belongs to the stronger. He who lives must rule. The Robots have gained the mastery. They have gained possession of life. We are masters of the world. . . . Room, room, more room for the Robots.'

As well as appearing in novels, robots (the android kind) have commonly crept into films. In most of these, the machines are nasty, menacing creatures. For instance, in *Target Earth!*, which was made in 1954, alien robots from another planet attempt to take over the world. *Zombies of the Stratosphere* (1952) and *Phantom Empire* (1935) are both based on adventures in space and the robots are again threatening. (*Star Wars*, made in 1977, is one of the few space-robot films where the robots are friendly, even lovable.) The most famous celluloid robot of them all is, of course, Frankenstein who is a most un-amiable character (though some people claim he is merely misunderstood).

Taking their cue from science fiction and the cinema, technicians of the 1920s and 1930s tried to make android robots in real life. The 1932 London Radio Exhibition featured several robots that could bow, make speeches and read newspapers. Among the most publicised was Alpha, which could tell the time in several languages. Eric, another robot, was created in the 1920s. He became famous by opening the 1928 exhibition of the Model Engineer Association with a neat little speech, made by courtesy of a loudspeaker in his throat.

Eric worked by a combination of electric motors, shafts and pulleys. Another well-known specimen of the genre was Elektro, made by Westinghouse of the US for a big exhibition in 1939 in New York. All these robots worked – in the limited jobs that they were called upon to do – and looked something like people, allowing for the fact that they were made of metal and walked somewhat stiffly. The machines owed their existence only partially to the inventive mind of Karel Capek and the trends he set in the play *R.U.R.* The androids of the 20th century had, in truth, predecessors in real life that stretch back several hundred years.

Intricate machines that imitate activities found in life (human or animal) appeared, particularly in France in the 17th and 18th centuries. Inventors made, for instance, walking, eating mechanical peacocks and models of people playing the organ. One inventor, Pierre Jacquet-Droz, was so good at making his 'robots' that, when he went to Spain in 1758, he was denounced as a sorcerer scarcely before he had had time to show off his wares.

One of the most famous automata – for this is probably a better word for the 'human-like' devices of the 18th century – was made by Baron Wolfgang von Kempelen. This was an automatic chess player in the form of a life-size model of a Turk, complete with turban and pipe, which sat in front of a chess board on top of a large desk. When opponents made a move, the 'Turk' contemplated for a few moments, then moved his own pieces with a mechanical hand. The German took his machine on a tour of several countries and it beat the best chess players that could be found. There were strong suspicions, however, that the device was a sham; the desk probably concealed a human midget who operated the 'Turk' with a series of rods.

Another well-known device of this kind was the mechanical lion that Leonardo da Vinci built around the year 1500 in honour of Louis XII. On a cue, the lion would walk toward the king, stop and then point ceremoniously to the coat of arms of France.

After the mechanical artefacts of earlier times had led to the generally rather nasty fictional robots of the early 20th century, it was left to science-fiction supremo Isaac Asimov to put in a good word for the machines. In his books, robots were not, as Asimov explained in 1981,* 'creaking Gothic menaces nor outlets for mawkish sentiment. They were simply well designed machines'. In

*In a forward to *Robotics in Practice*, by Joe Engelberger

Asimov's stories, the devices are made by an American company called Robot and Mechanical Men Inc. which employs a robo-psychologist to ensure the robots' brains function in a way that will not cause people problems. The science fiction maestro went so far as to draw up, in 1940, his famous Three Laws of Robotics, which are designed to ensure that robots will be always well disposed toward their human creators.*

Asimov, then, did much to turn the tide of popular opinion away from thinking that robots are always to be feared. Indirectly, he also did something far more important. He played a big part in influencing how robots changed from being toys, or unpaid actors in science-fiction movies, to become useful products that were to change how the world works.

It all started at a cocktail party in the eastern United States in 1956.

*Asimov's three laws are:–
1 A robot must not harm a human being, nor through inaction allow one to come to harm.
2 A robot must always obey human beings, unless that is in conflict with the first law.
3 A robot must protect itself from harm, unless that is in conflict with the first or second laws.

Chapter Eight
Robots march in

At the 1956 cocktail party was a 31-year-old engineer named Joe Engelberger. Most of Engelberger's career had been in the aerospace industry and he was getting bored. His mind was wandering toward those strange machines called robots. As a student, like many of his contemporaries, Engelberger had been much impressed by the stories of one Isaac Asimov and by the android-type robots that they described. But a hard-nosed engineer was hardly likely to dream that such machines could become fact – or was he?

Engelberger met at the gathering a man called George Devol, in Engelberger's words 'a wild-eyed inventor'.* The two men discussed a patent that Devol had taken out two years earlier which described a new kind of device for handling objects in factories.

'We had this wonderful idea,' Engelberger remembers. 'Why don't we make a machine for factory automation, but in a different way than it's normally done?'

Two years later, the conversation bore fruit. Engelberger and Devol made a machine that the latter's patent had described; it was the world's first industrial robot. In 1962, Engelberger formed a company called Unimation which, after many initial setbacks, went on to become the world's biggest robot firm.

In his 1981 book *Robotics in Practice*, Engelberger, still Unimation's president, paid homage to the science fiction of Asimov. And in a pleasant gesture, Asimov himself contributed the book's foreword. He wrote: 'I did not at that time [in the 1940s] seriously believe that I would live to see robots in action and robotics becoming a booming industry . . . Of course, the robots that now exist . . . are not yet as complex, versatile and intelligent as the imaginary

*Engelberger's quotes are taken from an interview with him in the Jan/Feb 1981 issue of the American magazine *Robotics Age*

robots of *I, Robot* [Asimov's famous collection of short stories] but give the engineers time!'

This veiled challenge by a doyen of science fiction to today's technicians is indeed being taken up, as later chapters will make clear.

Let us return to the proper subject for this book – industrial robots. Their major attribute is flexibility. Think of all the handling tasks that must be done in a factory – picking things up, painting, welding, putting objects together. Now it is not too difficult to devise automatic machines that do just one of these jobs; in this category come automatic welders or assembly devices that either weld or put together specific items. They cannot, however, be applied to other kinds of jobs – which makes their application in factory operations limited to companies that make products in large quantities and with unchanging designs. Such mechanisms belong to the era of 'inflexible' automation discussed earlier. What a boon it would be if someone came up with a flexible machine that could do a wide range of handling jobs. This is what the inventor George Devol had in mind when he took out his 1954 patent, titled 'programmed article transfer'.

Devol's patent, US number 2 988 237, describes a moving arm on wheels that unloads items from pallets into cartons; the exact operating method depends on instructions that are entered as code onto a magnetic drum. Depending on the instructions, the arm unloads the objects in a particular order and places them in batches in the waiting containers.

'The present invention,' Devol wrote in his patent, 'makes available for the first time a more or less general-purpose machine that has universal application to a vast diversity of applications where cyclic control is to be desired. . . . It makes an automatically operating machine available where previously it may not have been economical; . . . it makes possible the volume manufacture of universal automatic machines that are readily adaptable to a wide range of diversified applications; it makes possible the quick change-over of a machine adapted to any particular assignment so that it will perform new assignments.'

It was from Devol's phrase 'universal automation' that Engelberger got the idea for the name of his company – Unimation.

After Engelberger and Devol built their first machine in 1958, Engelberger tried to get the financial support to construct more. He took the idea to the Ford car company, which, as Chapter 2 pointed out, was much taken with the idea of new machinery for factories. Ford executive Del Harder, who is given the credit for inventing the word 'automation', understandably enthused about Engelberger's robot. He said he could use 2,000 of them almost immediately – if only someone would build them. Engelberger could not. He was still working for another company as Unimation had not yet been formed. So Ford took Engelberger's specification to established machinery companies and tried to persuade them to make the new devices. It was in this way that firms such as American Machine and Foundry (AMF), Borg-Warner and Hughes Tool started off making robots.

The first robot to start work in a factory was installed by Engelberger and some colleagues in 1961, a year before Unimation was officially formed. The machine unloaded hot pieces of metal from a die-casting machine in a car factory run by General Motors in Trenton, New Jersey. Thereafter, sales were slow; even by 1970, there were no more than seven hundred of the machines worldwide, of which some two hundred were in the US and one hundred and sixty in Japan. The 1970s were a decade of growth for robots: in 1974 the world contained 3,500; in 1978 the figure was 8,000; and in 1981 it was about 20,000. At this point, the world's robot population was doubling every two years; if the trend continues, as it shows every sign of so doing, the world will contain 200,000 robots by 1990. A robot costs anything between £5,000 and £100,000 depending on its function and complexity. Today there are dozens of firms all over the world that sell the machines, although the biggest are in either the US or Japan, in which countries more than half the world's total of robots are to be found.

Japan is the nation that has wedded itself most strongly to the idea of installing robots in factories; in 1981, it had about 8,000 of the devices, compared with 4,000 or so in the US. Figures quoted for robot installations in Japan are often much higher than this, as the Japanese have not accepted the American definition for the machines given earlier in this chapter; instead, they count as 'robots' virtually any mechanism that handles objects, even if the device is not programmable. In Western terminology, these simple machines are known as 'pick and place' devices. For instance, the *Japan Economic Journal* of 21 April 1981, said there were 70,000 robots in Japan, 'slightly over seventy per cent of the world market'. Some 12,000 new robots, worth 60 billion yen (about £120 million) were produced in 1980 in Japan, according to the terminology adopted in that country. The Japanese estimate that annual production will expand tenfold by 1990.

There is no doubt, however, about Japan's lead in the area of robots, and its commitment to keeping that lead. Japan has no less than one hundred and thirty makers of robots. Britain, by contrast, has about six.

Robots normally have six degrees of freedom; they can move about six different axes. The six degrees of freedom for a robot are illustrated in Figure 3. In this characteristic, the robot arm is emulat-

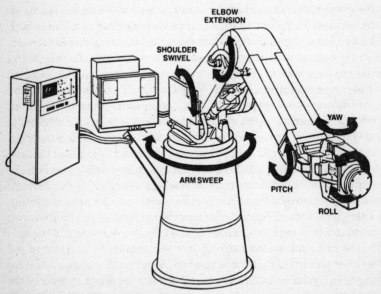

Fig. 3: Anatomy of a robot

ing what happens in a human arm. A human arm can, first, sweep in a horizontal plane from the shoulder; secondly, swivel from the shoulder in a vertical plane, as a bowler does when he delivers a cricket ball; thirdly, bend at the elbow; and, at the wrist, it can move in three more planes – here the arm can swivel, move up and down and move sideways. (Technically, these last three actions are known as roll, pitch and yaw; and of course, they are well known to yachtsmen.)

What other characteristics do robots have, remembering, of course, that we are talking about the straightforward robots that are found in factories today and not the more complex ones that may appear in the future? They have a 'hand', which is normally a lot less complex than the human hand with its fingers. The robot's device could be a simple claw with which it grips things; a vacuum pad for picking up objects; or an electromagnet for doing likewise with iron or steel. Engineers have even tried fitting a robot with fingers, each of which are separately controlled.

All robots – like people – need both a power source and a way of receiving instructions about the kind of movement that is required. In humans, the power source is carbohydrate stored in muscle which causes arms, legs and fingers to move; controlling this movement are messages from the brain which are transmitted to the muscles by the nervous system. Robots' operations follow a similar pattern. The power source can be one of three types: a pneumatic device by which the robot's upper and lower 'arm' moves by the force of compressed air; a hydraulic cylinder which acts in a similar way, only the force is transmitted through a pressurised liquid; or an electric motor. Strip a robot of its outer metallic casing, and you will find a 'skeleton' of rods and other linkages transmitting power from motors or from cylinders of compressed air or fluid to the device's extremities. Robots can be very strong: they can lift up to 1,000 kg. They can also be delicate. Some models can position an item with an accuracy of 1 mm.

The instructions determining how the robots move come in the form of electric signals passing along wires to the 'power' devices from the machine's control unit, which is normally a computer. In modern machines, it is not uncommon for the robot's movement in each of its six degrees of freedom to be controlled by a separate microprocessor.

In the computer, which normally manifests itself as a box that sits next to the robot's arm, is another vital part of the machine – an electronic memory. Stored in this are programs of instructions that give the robot its versatility. A robot can have any number of programs that let it do a wide variety of activities. An engineer puts the programs into the memory in one of two ways. First, he can enter data into it directly through a device such as a keyboard or a calculator-type pad. Thus if he wants the robot arm to move through a specific trajectory from one point to another – in the process, for instance, of picking up a piece of metal from a bench and putting it in a container – the operator would enter coordinates specifying these points by punching numbers on the keyboard. Resident software – internal sequences of instructions that are always present inside the computer – would translate these raw numbers into commands that tell the robot to move in a combination of its six degrees of freedom to bring about the desired movement.

The second way of getting data into the memory is by what robot engineers call 'teaching by doing'. This is a quaint-sounding, though extremely useful, technique that has added to the anthropomorphic nature of robots. The operator simply guides the robot arm gently with his hand through the sequence of actions that he wants it to 'remember'; the computer memory recalls the positions that the arm moves into and, when activated on a later occasion, the memory releases instructions to get the robot to do as it has been told. The technique is most useful for instructing a robot to do highly skilled jobs, painting a piece of metal with a complicated shape for instance. A person guides the robot (suitably armed with a paint sprayer in its gripper) through the sequence of arm actions that he would take in doing the painting; the machine recalls this and, when pressed into service later, repeats the same action time after time (while jetting out paint from the spray gun) until told to stop. Unlike the person, the robot is consistent and will not, by losing concentration, deviate from the optimum way of painting.

Programmed with a library of instructions, whose size is limited only by the storage space inside the computer memory, the robot is extremely flexible. By changing the program, an operator can switch it between painting, welding, picking things up and so on. Such alterations in job functions would, of course, require the person to change the tool that the machine holds in its gripper and also the ancillary apparatus – fixtures that hold the items being painted or welded for instance – that surround it. So it is more likely that the operator would merely change the robot's movement while keeping the activity the same; in this way, for instance, a machine could be made to paint different sizes of frames for washing machines or, in a car factory, pick up axle housings and put them in a variety of bins.

You should now be getting a picture of the kind of jobs that robots are capable of doing. Spraying paint, welding, picking things up and putting them in trays or on pallets, loading machine tools, taking metal parts out of forges or die-casting machines – these are the commonest applications. There are also a few more unusual jobs.

Chesebrough Pond's in Clinton, Connecticut, is loading bottles onto a conveyor with a robot; the bottles travel round to a machine that fills them with face cream. Here the robot saves a person doing the job; and because it is programmable, an engineer can easily switch his machine between different kinds of tasks. Thus it can be loading bottles one day; with the necessary adjustments, a week later it could be stacking cans of lipsticks onto a pallet.

Also in the US, a company called United Space Boosters wants to use a robot to clean parts of NASA's space shuttle when they fall onto the Earth during the space vehicle's flight. A re-useable launcher, the shuttle will be cost-effective only if, after each launch, parts of it can be cleaned up and put together again to make new vehicles. The robot does its job by shooting high-pressure jets of water at the shuttle's booster sections to clear off bits of charred metal and damaged protective layers. The reason for introducing the machine here is that people might hurt themselves by holding the high-pressure jets; if directed at the eyes or other sensitive parts of the body these can cause a lot of damage.

In York, England, the chocolate company Rowntree Mackintosh is experimenting with robots to load boxes of confectionery. Normally this job is done by lines of people, usually women, who are each given a container full of one type of chocolate. A series of boxes speeds past them on a conveyor and each person puts a chocolate in the appropriate section until, by the end of the line, all the boxes are full up. This is hardly stimulating work; but, more to the point, Rowntree Mackintosh thinks it can save money by replacing people with machines, specially as the latter can work twenty-four hours a day and don't get tired. In another unusual application in the UK, the Scottish firm Lyle and Scott wants robots to help in making underpants. The robots will grab parts of the garments and pass them to sewing machines.

Another set of robots works away in the cathedral city of Wells, Somerset, welding supermarket trolleys for a company called WCB Clares. The robots make about four times as many good welds per day than a person, mainly because they are more consistent. Initially, the firm had trouble making the fixtures (that hold the trolley parts) accurate enough for robots. Whereas human welders can see what they are doing and make adjustments to a routine if the part that they are supposed to be welding is positioned wrongly, a robot repeats over and again a set routine, oblivious of changes that may have taken place around it. This is one of the drawbacks about robots – though engineers are trying to find ways of overcoming it, as we shall see in the next chapter. Anyhow, WCB Clares took nine months to tighten up tolerances and then increased production by forty-two per cent in two years mainly as a result of greater efficiency due to the new machines.

Yet another area where robots come in useful is in unloading injection moulding equipment, in which chemicals are squeezed into a mould and allowed to set for a specific time; someone, or something, then has to take out the finished item, which could be a plastic water tank or a bucket. The firm of Wavin Plastics in Durham bought a robot for this and thinks that the machine 'paid for itself' in a year. Not only did the machine save the company employing a person to do the task, it led to fewer defective products. Unlike a person, who loses concentration and is not consistent, the machine removes the moulded item always a set time after the chemicals have been pumped into the machine. Hence a robot-tended machine will produce a greater percentage of properly finished items than one tended by a person. The use of robots in this area of work seems to have great potential; a small Birmingham firm, Mouldmation, has been formed to concentrate on selling this type of device.

Meanwhile in Middle Wallop, a little village in Hampshire, another robot is loading boxes of explosives in a factory run by Wallop Industries. The job, no one will be surprised to hear, is not very pleasant for people – and it can be dangerous too.

In Basingstoke, Hampshire, a team of engineers who work for the fork-lift truck firm Lansing Bagnall have perfected a most useful application for a robot. The job entails threading lengths of wire to form what are called wiring harnesses; these form the electrical 'backbone' of many kinds of electrical appliances – anything between industrial trucks and cookers. Normally, people have to do the job. They thread the wires around pins on a board about the size of a table top.

When the harness is complete – each one can contain twenty or so different wires threaded around perhaps one hundred pins – the worker ties it with tape, lifts it from the pins and gets on with the next harness. The process is slow and, even more to the point, boring. With great imagination, the engineers at Lansing Bagnall have programmed a robot to make the harnesses; the machine is so versatile it can even insert the pins in the board in an infinite number of patterns depending on the design of the harness that is required.

Vacuum cleaners are among the many household goods that are made, at least partly, with robots. In one of Hoover's plants in North Canton, Ohio, robots lift parts from a moulding machine and load them onto a conveyor. The machines help in a similar fashion in a diecasting works run by Metal Castings in Worcester, England, which turns out parts for kitchen equipment. And at ICI's works in Fleetwood, robots load onto wooden pallets heavy sacks of chemicals of the kind which end up in many commonplace products as plastics.

But it is in car factories that robots have been welcomed most enthusiastically. As we have seen, it was General Motors, the car giant whose annual turnover is roughly equivalent to a quarter of

Britain's annual output of goods and services, which installed the very first industrial robot. Ten years later, in 1971, the firm employed a group of twenty-six robots in a plant in Lordstown, Ohio: it was the first big plunge by any company into serious application of the devices.

The robots at Lordstown were used for spot welding – the most common application of robots in car factories. During the manufacture of a vehicle, there are six main stages: machining of items such as cylinder blocks and casings by machine tools or transfer lines; the cutting and beating-out of panels for the vehicle's exterior; the welding of these panels to the chassis; painting in a special paint shop; engine and gearbox assembly; and the fixing, to the newly constructed body, of the engine and gearbox together with the dozens of other components that make up the complete car – wheels, bumpers, seats, windows, door handles, wing mirrors and so on.

It is only in the third and fourth stages (and sometimes the first) that robots are useful. In the other parts of making a car, people are still indispensable, at least for the present. Especially in assembly: here, car factories have not progressed that far from the assembly lines of Henry Ford's day. So anyone who talks about cars being 'handbuilt by robots', as Fiat has done in TV advertisements, is being misleading.

On a robot welding line, a car body is first 'tacked' together with small, insubstantial bits of metal. The body enters one end of the line on a conveyor, which hauls it past a row of perhaps a dozen or so robots armed with welding guns. Each robot is programmed to apply a particular sequence of welds – a series that fixes the top of the car to one of its sides, for instance – and does so, over and again, for each body that travels past on the conveyor. Several hundred welds after entering the line, a body emerges, this time firmly joined together.

From here, the basic shell of the vehicle will probably pass to a line of automatic, special-purpose painting machines. These are *not* robots. They spray paint in a specified way, for instance at the roof of a body of a fixed shape, and cannot be reprogrammed for other applications. Therefore, they are useful for only certain models of vehicles; the machines belong very definitely to the category of 'inflexible automation'. But besides these machines, the paint shop will also contain a line of robots that *are* reprogrammable. The robots are suitably armed with spray guns and will do the painting jobs that the special-purpose machines find too difficult. For instance, a robot could use its jointed arm to wriggle inside a car body to paint a section that is difficult to get at and which would normally require the dexterity of a human. Alternatively, the robot could switch quickly between spraying different colours, or between painting a range of vehicle bodies whose shapes vary.

Although General Motors pioneered the use of robots in car factories, other firms in the same business were quick to follow. Chrysler, Ford, Toyota, Volvo, Renault, Volkswagen – all are very big users of robots. The final two even build their own. Fiat made headlines with its special Robogate welding system which, as well as installing in some plants in Italy, it has exported to the US and Eastern Europe. And in 1980, Britain, rather slow to build cars with robots, finally got into the act when British Leyland installed a robot welding line in its Longbridge, Birmingham, factory. In the same year, Ford of UK started robot welding in its Halewood plant. General Motors alone more than doubled the number of robots that it owns in the six months to April 1981, at which point its total stood at 1,100. The car company plans to install a total of 5,000 robots by 1985, and a massive 14,000 by 1990.

Just to show the dominance of the car firms in the US robot industry, the market researcher Creative Strategies International estimates that three-quarters of the 1980 US sales of 'heavy-duty' robots – machines for jobs such as welding or die-casting – were in the car industry. Overall, the market research firm expects sales in this area to grow from £9 million in 1980 to seven times this figure in 1985. In the area of 'light' robots – which do less arduous tasks such as lifting objects into machine tools – the projected rise in sales is even greater. The figure should leap from £8.5 million in 1980 to £190 million in 1985.

Don't be fooled into thinking that it is just the heavyweights of the industrial world which are turning to robots. A number of firms, particularly in the US, are selling robots that people can make, play with and even give useful jobs – in their homes. Robot Mart, a firm in New York, sells a machine called a Turtle which looks like a small toy and rolls about the floor according to a program of instructions in its computer memory. More ambitious, and twice as expensive, is the $800 Unicorn which is the size of a five-year-old: it can move around on treads and can pick things up. Another company, the Android Amusement Corporation of Monrovia, California, sells for almost $5,000 – a little too expensive for most home computer freaks – what the company calls a 'drinks caddy robot' which hands out beverages from a bar. The move toward robots that can walk around the home is not confined to the US. In Twickenham, near London, a company called Colne Robotics sells a little robot that costs just £200 and can be driven by a home computer such as a Pet or an Apple.

Turning again to the world of big business, how exactly do manufacturers justify the use of robots? First, they save a company labour costs: one robot will do the work of a person, or two people, if the factory operates for two shifts per day. What is more the machine will probably do the job better, assuming that the task is suitable. It does not have meal breaks, lose concentration, get sick or visit the toilet. As labour costs rise and the price of robots stabilises, or in some cases goes down, it is not uncommon for a machine to recover its costs within two years. But much the same could be said of special-purpose, inflexible machines, which, for instance, take out objects of a specified size from a die-casting machine or load lumps of metal of the same shape into a machine tool. So what makes a robot more useful than these machines?

Joe Engelberger gives three reasons. Firstly, robots' flexibility – the fact that they can be reprogrammed to do different jobs – makes it straightforward for manufacturers to slot them into factories, specially when setting up new lines. This is particularly the case in car factories where it is very important that manufacturers can switch over to make new models relatively painlessly. With a line of robot welders, a car company can quickly change between assembling different kinds of car bodies; sometimes, it can even put together two or three different bodies simultaneously. Such an opportunity is denied to the firm that uses special-purpose machines; if it decides to build a welding shop for a new model, it either has to scrap its current welding devices and buy new ones, or spend a lot of time and money altering them.

The second reason, according to Engelberger, is that, with a robot manufacturing system, less time and effort has to be spent ensuring that the system works properly after it has been delivered onto a factory floor. With ordinary inflexible automation, after delivery engineers must expend a lot of energy ensuring that the system's components – devices such as part-feeders, clamping mechanisms and actuators – operate free from errors and in synchronisation. Each part has been specially built and adapted for only one industrial process. With robots, on the other hand, much of this 'debugging' has been done already in the robot maker's factory. Engineers there have tested the equipment thoroughly; they can afford to spend the time and effort on this, because they know that, once they have got their machines working properly, the devices will be able to do virtually any job. To do the same amount of debugging for every piece of special-purpose equipment that emerges from a machinery maker's factory would simply cost the firm too much money.

The third advantage is that robots resist obsolescence. The fact that engineers can continually adapt them to new processes means that they rarely get scrapped – at least in Engelberger's view. Thus a robot can be useful until it literally wears out, unlike special-purpose machines which frequently get thrown out of factories, due to product changes, long before they are mortised.

Robot makers themselves are a disparate bunch. Most of them started in the business after seeing what other robot companies were doing; thus most can trace their parentage, directly or indirectly, to Unimation's creation of the industry back in the 1960s. Some companies – AMF of the US for instance – reacted directly to the ideas of Engelberger and Devol. This company brought out a robot called Versatran, which is now sold by Prab. Other firms realised that they could use robots in their own manufacturing processes, decided to make them and then realised they were on to a good thing and sold the machines to outside users. In this category are Tralfa of Norway, Electrolux of Sweden (which has since merged its robot interests with Asea, also of Sweden), Renault, Volkswagen and a clutch of Japanese companies – Mitsubishi, Hitachi and Fujitsu Fanuc for instance.

Yet more robot firms make the devices solely for their own manufacturing plants, and are very secretive about what their machines actually do. These firms, which ward off inquiries about sales to outsiders, include the giant Texas Instruments of the US, which uses its machines in the potentially very big business of assembling products (of which more in the next chapter). Other companies got into the business by seeing the robot industry is going to be big and taking out licences on other firms' devices, first merely selling the machines and then making the hardware themselves. In this category are General Electric of the US – which is selling, as well as using in its own plants, the Pragma robot made by DEA of Italy and also robots developed by Volkswagen – and Fairy Automation of the UK. In 1982, IBM, the world's biggest computer firm, announced it would sell a Japanese robot under licence. It will also sell a more advanced machine developed by its own engineers for assembling typewriters. IBM was quickly followed by another giant – General Motors – which will sell robots developed by Fujitsu Fanuc of Japan.

Finally, we have examples of firms that see robots as extensions of their businesses in other areas of industrial machinery. Cincinnati Milacron of the US, one of the world's biggest machine tool firms, set about designing a robot in 1969. It developed a prototype in 1974, starting selling the machine in 1977, and by 1981 was challenging Unimation for the title of the world's number-one robot manufacturer. Another example is Fujitsu Fanuc of Japan which also makes controls for machine tools: the computers which are part of the most modern machine tools are very similar, if not the same, as the controls for robots.

Britain made a surprisingly good start in robots – but then fell away. In the 1960s, the UK's robot population compared favourably with the US's. But by 1978, it was still less than one hundred, compared with several thousand in the US. By 1981, according to a British Robot Association survey, there were just over seven hundred robots in the UK. For many years, Britain's sole robot manufacturer was Hall Automation of Watford.

Doug Hall, the firm's founder, has had a long, though somewhat chequered, career in robots. He set up robot divisions in Hawker Siddely and Pye Dynamics – both of which folded through lack of interest by the parent company – before setting up his own company in 1974. Thereafter, Hall struggled to sell many machines to UK manufacturers, who displayed their long-standing indifference to factory technology (a relic of the Victorian attitude here). The company existed mainly on exports of a few dozen machines per year, mainly for painting or welding. Hall's dream of getting more cash with which to develop and market his robots came true in 1979 when GEC, Britain's electrical giant, purchased his company. GEC said it would pour cash into the firm – although how much this amounts to, and what the results will be, still seems uncertain.

In 1981, Britain was making a belated effort to get into the big league in robot making. The Department of Industry promised that persuading firms to use the devices was an area of high priority. Grants became available to companies prepared to employ the machines in new applications – and for those willing to take the plunge and swell the ranks of UK robot manufacturers. A delegation from the British government visited Japan in the summer of 1981 to discuss possible deals in which UK companies make or sell Japanese robots. Sykes and the 600 Group are among the British firms engaged in either of these two activities. With engineers all round the world anxious to visit Japan to learn the latest developments in robots, the country must be reflecting that a slow start in a technology should not necessarily prevent rapid progress later on. The first firm to make robots in a big way in Japan was Kawasaki; and it began this only in 1968. The Japan Industrial Robot Association was formed as recently as 1971.

Robots are still far from being uncontroversial, even in Japan. People still fear – with some justification – that the machines can do away with their jobs. After all, the main reason for employing a robot is that it does a job better than a human. The argument really hinges – as do all debates about automation – on whether, by employing new machinery, a firm will become more efficient and win orders, so safeguarding the jobs of its employees in general –

not just those on the shop floor but everywhere else as well. According to protagonists of robots, the machines may mean unemployment for those doing the work that the equipment takes over, but, in the long run, they may well preserve jobs.

With three million unemployed in the early 1980s, it is small wonder that the fear of robots in Britain remains high. Trade unionists think that the machines probably are necessary in the cause of raising productivity and making the country more competitive. But many believe that the extra unemployment caused by the machines may be virtually impossible to combat in view of the numbers of those already out of work.

The arguments surfaced at an otherwise genteel event in October 1981 when the Department of Industry unveiled a film it has made to persuade industrialists to use more robots. Academics and trade unionists harangued each other about the social effects of the devices. When one professor commented that the machine had never put anyone out of work, the earthy response came back: 'You must have been living on the Moon.'

The debate is not confined to Britain. Japan is the world's leading user of robots, and has one of the smallest rates of unemployment. But it, too, has grave doubts about the future effects of the machines. It is worth quoting at length from the *Japan Economic Journal* of 19 October 1981: 'For the time being, an overwhelming majority of people seem to be supporting the introduction of robots, saying the immediate impact of robot introduction upon employment is very light. We also support this trend. As the world's technological power (sic) Japan is in a position to further promote technological innovation in electronics and other fields, making greater use of robots to replace dangerous and tedious work and increase productivity . . .

'But despite this favourable position, a problem remains as to whether this favourable environment for introducing robots will continue for ever. It depends on the pace of overall economic growth in the future, but it is safe to say that the Japanese economy will steadily lose room to absorb workers displaced by robots in the long run . . .

'Seen in the long run and the level of individual firms and industries, robots will have a serious impact upon employment. In addition, when robots begin to have "eyes" and can point out parts and spots to work on, they will become "intelligent robots" and will be able to do complex work. They could possibly generate serious situations in the future.'

The writer of the editorial is alluding to the possibility that before long much more useful 'intelligent' robots will appear. Because their capabilities are much higher than the current versions of the devices, they will threaten employment levels even more. Already, in fact, such equipment is emerging from the research laboratories. The machines have an anthropomorphic feature that some may find alarming. They can see what they are doing.

Chapter Nine
The seeing machine

The first robot with elementary vision – apart that is, from all the ones which had featured previously in science-fiction books – was put together in a small laboratory in Britain's industrial heartland in 1973. In 1981, just one British firm made vision equipment for robots. The rest of the world contained a dozen or more, many of which were investing prodigious sums in research to develop their techniques further. If robot vision turns out to be as revolutionary as its advocates promise, it will be other countries, not the UK, which reap the benefits.

The story is worth dwelling on because it illustrates a familiar failing in British industry. Often, engineers in the UK have bright ideas which fall on stony ground at home but which are taken up with enthusiasm elsewhere.

The first 'seeing' robot was called SIRCH – it stands for Semi-Intelligent Robot for Component Handling. It was developed at the University of Nottingham's production engineering laboratory. The equipment was rudimentary and would never have worked in a factory. But the principles that it used were basically those which any robot with sight, now or in the future, will employ.

If it were assembled today from its components, which are stacked away in corners of laboratories around the UK, SIRCH would comprise a gripper that can move in several directions above a small stand on which is positioned an object, a metal plate for instance. Next to the gripper is a TV camera that inspects the object and relays information about it to the computer that controls the gripper's mechanism. In this way, the robot (for that is what the gripper plus computer add up to) learns about the object's shape and position and, if so instructed by a program inside the computer, moves in such a way to pick up the object. From a random position, SIRCH would take about five seconds to locate and manipulate an object.

The device was engineered under the supervision of Professor Wilf Heginbotham, who is today the director-general of the Production Engineering Research Association in Melton Mowbray. Heginbotham is sad that his device was not developed to the point that it could be marketed. In Britain, industrial sponsors never enthused about the hardware. But in the US it was a different story.

The Nottingham engineers went to California's Stanford University to lecture about their achievement. The audience was impressed. In the words of one former Nottingham researcher, 'They told us to stop messing about and start selling the system.' The advice fell on deaf ears. But the news about the British device spurred engineers at Stanford to develop their own vision gadget. Today, SRI International, a company that was formed several years ago from researchers at Stanford, sells a vision module that can be connected to robots to make them see. The principles that it uses closely resemble those harnessed in SIRCH.

Giving a robot vision is one way of equipping it with 'sense' so it will be more useful. Machines of this kind, which react to changes taking place around them, are called 'second generation' robots.

Why are they useful? Think of the applications for robots discussed in the last chapter. Welding cars, painting bits of metal, picking things up and putting them on conveyors – all are jobs that such a 'first generation' robot does according to a fixed pattern of instructions, which tells the device's arm to move in a set way. At work in a factory, the robot spends all day on a particular job, repeating its routine time after time. For instance, when welding together identical pairs of components in a workshop, the robot works away perfectly happily, so long as new pairs are presented to it at regular intervals, and always in the same position. Problems occur, however, if a piece of metal is presented in a place different to the one that the machine expects.

There are many applications for robots where engineers find it simple to present objects to them in positions that are predetermined. For instance, with mechanisms called jigs that hold things very accurately in place, an engineer can ensure that a robot is always given objects in positions accurate to a millimetre or so.

But it is seldom cheap to set up such equipment: often the special ancillary hardware will cost more than the robot itself. And there are many other applications where it would be much simpler and cheaper to give the robot a batch of parts in any order and in any orientation, and leave it to get on with the job in hand, whether this be welding, stacking or anything else. To work under these conditions, the robot would have to possess sense in a similar way as people.

Imagine a deaf, dumb and blind person trying to do a straightforward job in a factory, loading parts into a box for example. Now think of a person with all his or her senses intact doing the same task. Then you have the difference between the robots of the last chapter and the new, enhanced 'second-generation' machines.

But how do you give a machine 'sense'? Here engineers have unashamedly borrowed from the way that humans perceive their surroundings. People do this through 'sensors' such as eyes, ears, noses and nerve endings. These organs feed the information to the brain which analyses it and decides what the body's legs, arms and so on should do on account of it. It is the same with robots. A 'sensing' robot must first have sensors, which take note of what is happening near the machine and feed the data so obtained to a central 'brain', which, for a robot, is a computer. The latter then unscrambles the information and sends new instructions to the robot's manipulator, for instance, to tell it the shape of parts travelling towards it on a conveyor and the correct time at which to pick them up.

The most straightforward sensor for robots is a TV camera which acts as the machine's 'eyes'. There are more engineers working on this area of robot 'sense' than any other. But you can also find engineers beavering away in research laboratories in efforts to give robots touch and hearing. No doubt there are also robots on the drawing board which have the sense of smell.

Described in a couple of paragraphs, it sounds almost childishly simple to give a robot sense. Hook it up to a TV camera, arrange for the data to flow from camera to computer to robot and back again – in other words to establish a 'feedback' loop of the kind seen in the human body – and you have a 'seeing' robot.

However, several major problems make the job more difficult

than you might think. Engineers have a long way to go before they devise machines that come anywhere near a person in their ability to take note of events around them and act accordingly. (For more about the problem of perception, see Chapters 11 and 12). The first difficulty is that researchers have to devise a way of coding easily comprehensible (for computers) signals that the components in the feedback loop can pass between themselves. Secondly, the sensors must be sufficiently aware of what is happening near the robot to give it meaningful information; but they must not be too sensitive that they pass floods of information to the computer brain and so overload it.

A third difficulty is that the computer has to process its data extraordinarily quickly. Unless this happens, the computer may instruct the manipulator in the loop too late for the information to be any use. With data that arrive too late, the system would be in a similar position to a person with a brain malfunction who, entering a café and passed a cup of tea, stretches out his hand to take it, not instantaneously, but half a minute or so afterwards. If you think how difficult life must be for such people, you realise how important it is for the developers of 'sensing' robots to make their devices perceive things quickly. In practice, this means ensuring that a robot's TV camera receives an image, decides what it represents and passes the information onto the manipulator – all in one-tenth of a second or less. Such demands require computing power of enormous capacity. One of the reasons for the growth in recent years of research into robots with sense is that the computing power required for this job, thanks to cheap microelectronics, has become reasonably inexpensive. Only ten or fifteen years ago, computers that could process information with the speeds required hardly existed, and where they did, they took up the space of a room and cost hundreds of thousands of pounds, well beyond the budgets of all but the most well-endowed researchers. Today, massive computer power can reside in just a few chips that, together with ancillary equipment, fit into the space of a shoebox.

There is a fourth problem area for the designers of the new robots. They have to design the mechanical parts of their machines – the robot's arm and grippers – in such a way that the devices can do

85

the complex and delicate jobs demanded of them. It is no good having a superb method of relaying information from the outside world to the robot, together with an ultra-fast computer brain to cope with this information, if the manipulator cannot do its job properly. This is a lesson that has been learnt by many outside the disciplines of electronics and mechanical engineering. The world is full of frustrated artists who have what they think are brilliant ideas for, say, paintings or sculptures. The designs no doubt exist in what may well be a superbly well-oiled brain, but these people completely lack the manual dexterity to put their ideas into practice. In robot terminology, their gripper design and control is absolutely hopeless.

A crucial part of designing a seeing robot is the way in which images of the outside world are coded so that they mean something to the robot. Robots are controlled by computers which operate according to an electronic language of binary digits. The only symbols that computers understand are the numbers 0 and 1. Therefore, information sent to them has to be put into the form of an electric current that comprises sequences of pulses, corresponding to the 1s in the language, separated by breaks in the current that signify the 0s. A taxing task for the research engineer is to devise a way of translating the rich, multidimensional experience of life into a dry sequence of binary digits so that robots can understand, to some extent at least, the events that take place around them.

Just as the retinas of our eyeballs, however, codify the pictures that they receive of the outside world into flashes of current that pass along nerves to the brain, so it is possible to do a similar job for 'seeing' robots. Images from the TV camera are passed to a special-purpose computer called a picture processor. This is normally separate from a second computer which controls the robot's arm (see Figure 4). The picture processor analyses its images in one of several ways. In one technique, it breaks up pictures into a series of tiny squares and assigns to each one a binary number according to whether the square is black or white (this assumes the picture is not in colour). The method is similar to that used by wire agencies to transmit photographs along telephone lines to newspapers. The picture processor then has stored in its memory a collection of binary digits that corresponds to the picture of the outside world that has just flashed before the camera. Another method of analysis is for the picture processor to search through the image for edges of objects, or their centres. Through this, the computer can work out the shape of items in the picture.

To make any sense of the information so obtained, the processor then has to match it with other data held in its memory. Here, the computer holds a 'file' of pictures of the objects that its operator thinks it will encounter. The pictures are stored as a series of binary digits. By comparing the pictures that it has just received with those in its memory, the processor is able to recognise things. For instance, think of a robot working away in somebody's kitchen doing the washing up. (I am not suggesting that robots can do this kind of job today, but, who knows, in a few years they may do.) To understand the objects that it has to wash, the machine's picture processor would contain images of, say, wine glasses, cups, saucers, plates and so on. When a new item swims into sight, the processor would swiftly match its image with those stored in its brain until it

Fig. 4: Robot with vision

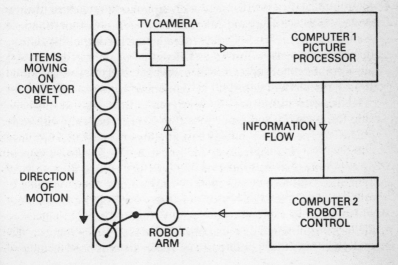

finds one that correlates exactly. It is then able to discover that the object it next has to deal with is, say, a teapot, as opposed to a milk jug.

As well as identifying things in this way, a robot with vision will find out other information about the objects scanned by the TV camera. For instance, other processing steps determine objects' positions and their orientation. A complete set of data about objects near the robot is then passed to the second computer in the system, which controls the robot's manipulator. The information is added to instructions in this computer's memory that tell the robot mechanism about the jobs that the operator wants it to perform. Instead of repeating its task time after time, oblivious to changes that are taking place around it, the robot will do the job in a way that takes into account this extra information. For instance, in picking a package off a conveyor, it will receive details about the item's shape and position before getting ready to grab it, or in the hypothetical case of the 'washing-up' robot, armed with the information that the object in front of it is a teacup and not a milk bottle, the machine would grasp, and then wash, the item in the correct way.

Companies are now selling vision modules that can be added to robots to impart the useful capability of seeing. As well as SRI International, other firms that sell vision modules include Brown Boveri of Switzerland and Machine Intelligence Corporation and Auto-Place of the US. Systems Programming Ltd is the British firm that sells products in this area. Unimation of the US, the world's most prolific robot supplier, is also working hard on 'vision' robots. It is particularly interested in equipping with vision its PUMA machine, a small, electrically-driven machine that is specially suitable for assembly and other jobs that have to be done with high precision. The vision modules cost anything from £5,000 upwards and have varying degrees of sophistication. Thus some recognise objects only if they are of clearcut shape; others have limited memories so that they can identify only a small range of objects; others require the objects that they are viewing to be illuminated with intense light, or to be on specially coloured backgrounds. Still the biggest limitation on the application of such seeing robots is the speed at which they operate; many vision systems need as long as one second to identify things which is far too much for application in factories.

The most impressive aspect about work with the new 'second generation' machines is the number of organisations around the world doing research in this area. Many of these have no wish to sell 'seeing' machines to outsiders. They want instead to use vision systems in their own factories to increase the efficiency with which they make their products. Such companies include some of the giants of the industrial world. Texas Instruments and IBM are already using simple 'seeing' robots in their factories to do jobs such as picking items off conveyors or putting together the parts of typewriters. General Motors, which has developed a vision system called Consight, plans to link it to robots that lift castings off conveyors. The vision equipment will determine the shape of parts and whether they are defective.

Renault is another company that is doing plenty of work on robot vision. Since 1974, engineers at its Billancourt research laboratories near Paris have worked on this problem. One possibility under consideration is to put a seeing robot in a factory to watch a random series of parts flowing past on a conveyor. When specified parts come past that have a characteristic shape and size, the robot picks them up and inserts them into a machine tool for cutting or drilling.

One of the biggest applications for 'seeing' robots is in assembling things. Often, this is a job that has to be done with great precision. You would appreciate this if you have ever tried, for instance, to put together a subassembly in the control mechanism of a washing machine – a typical assembly job done in factories. To do such a task, the robot manipulator would have to handle things with both dexterity and accuracy. Furthermore, it is often not possible i `small-scale assembly operations – putting together the parts of an electric motor for instance – to present the components in always the same positions to enable an orthodox 'first generation' or 'deaf, dumb and blind' robot to do the job. In this kind of activity, robots with vision or other senses are often vital if the job is to be automated.

There is plenty of scope for replacing people in assembly operations with machines. In some mass-production industries, assembly jobs are often just about the only factory jobs left that are impossible to automate with conventional equipment. In a car factory, for instance, the assembly line, where people add fittings and components to the basic vehicle shell, is the most labour-intensive part of the operation. According to figures from the 1970 census in the US, 33 per cent of the employees in car factories are assembly workers. The figures for farm equipment and for TV and radio receivers are thirty and twenty-three per cent respectively.

When a factory has to assemble anything, from a carburettor to a mechanism in a vacuum cleaner, it has three options. It can either pay a person to do the job; it can design a special-purpose machine that will do the task perfectly well, but cannot be reprogrammed to make variations on a standard product; or it can use a robot.

The assembly worker is wonderfully flexible on account of his marvellous actuators (hands) and superb control mechanism (brain). But his running costs (wages) are, in many countries, very high, and increasing. The special-purpose machine contains expensive jigs, fixtures and part-feeders. As well as being costly it is highly inflexible; it will generally be useful only if the product it is assembling is required at the rate of a million or so per year and will not be changed, to meet fluctuations in consumer taste, for at least two or three years. Only a few products fall into this category. Which explains why, according to Professor Geoffrey Boothroyd of the University of Massachusetts, only four to six per cent of assembled products in factories are made with automatic machinery. The rest rely on humans or on semi-automatic equipment.

This leaves the third alternative – the largely uncharted territory of robots. You do not necessarily need sight to assemble things with robots. In the mid 1970s, researchers at the Charles Stark Draper Laboratory in Cambridge, Massachusetts, built a one-arm assembly system that can put together an alternator by stacking its seventeen parts on top of each other. Crucially, this could handle changes in design. It could be reprogrammed to make the alternators in different styles, just as a real factory would need, to put into different models of car.

But other workers think that to be properly flexible, robot assembly devices will require vision. This attribute means that

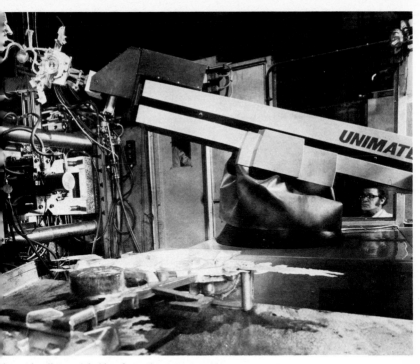

bot unloading metal object from die casting machine.

ting a sack of chemicals with a robot with a suction gripper

A robot welds the parts of a supermarket trolley

Above right: Robots in a chocolate factory: an engineer adjusts a machine that automatically puts sweets in their right position in boxes

Teaching a robot welder how to operate

ɔbot loads bottles into boxes

ɛr putting pegs in this table, the robot threads around them wires that eventually form wiring ɪnesses

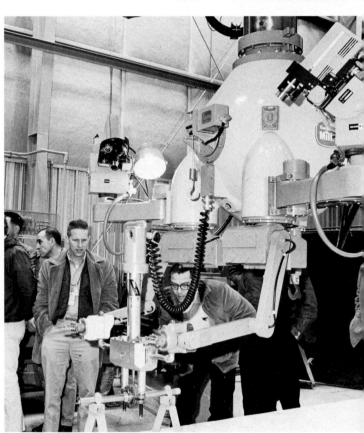

SIRCH, the world's first 'seeing' robot devised at Nottingham University in the 1960s

Prototype of some of today's intelligent robots. This dates to the 1960s: it inspects equipment in nuclear reactors

modern computer-controlled machine tool

ove right: This machining centre drills or cuts objects that are placed on pallets
the rotating table in front of it. It can select tools from either of the two 'carousels' on either
e

'seeing' robot is put through its paces at General Motor's research laboratories

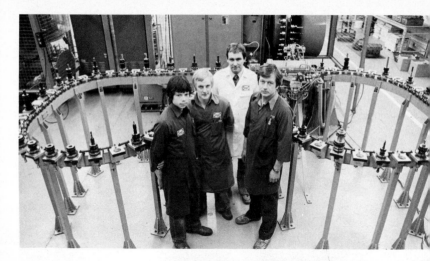

Operators at the Crewkerne factory of Normalair Garrett, the scene of one of the UK's first flexible manufacturing systems. The tools on the rollers behind the group supply the machining centre in the background.

This robot is loading and unloading from a number of unmanned machine tools

Robot welding line at BL's Metro factory in Longbridge

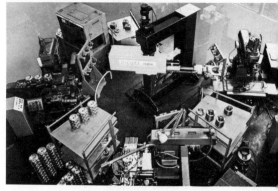

The US Navy's prototype unmanned submarine – the craft has sensors which will let it assess for itself which way to travel to underwater pipelines

Fiat's Robogate factory in Turin

The remote-controlled truck in the foreground shuttles to and from machining centres (such as the one in the background) and thus plays a big part in the factory's flexible manufacturing system.

Intelligent robot developed at London's Queen Mary College. This 'sees' where it is going with a TV camera and can navigate around a room

Above right:
Commander Bill, an unmanned robot truck developed at Warwick University

Robot with human hand.

engineers have to spend less time and money devising a lot of jigs and fixtures to hold, for presentation to the robot, parts that will often alter owing to design changes in the final product. The most publicised assembly project is run by Westinghouse at its research laboratory in Pittsburgh. The £1 million programme, partly paid for by the US's National Science Foundation, is constructing a robot system that will put together the fifty or so parts of an electric motor. The complete system will have as many as a dozen robots, some of them with vision, which put together subassemblies from parts fed to them along conveyors. By reprogramming the computer, or rather the series of computers, that control the system, engineers will be able to instruct the machinery to turn out motors of different styles. This is an essential characteristic if the assembly mechanism is to be any good for a motor manufacturer that makes dozens of different types of motors per day to fit into equipment as varied as dishwashers and cars. Westinghouse's engineers think that if all goes to plan, a fully engineered version of their equipment could be working in the company's factories in 1983 or 1984.

Another key area where the new 'second generation' robots with vision or some other kind of sense could make headway is in the food and toiletries industry. Firms in this business make and package a lot of small items that are loaded on or off conveyors during some part of the manufacturing operation. For instance, in making bottles of shampoo or bars of soap, a lot of the work is in either wrapping the product or lifting it on or off belts. Often, there are changes in the shape or style of the product – for instance a soap manufacturer might suddenly decide to make his bars slightly bigger or smaller – which means that flexible, rather than orthodox inflexible automatic machinery is required. This leads directly to robots. Machines with vision would be particularly useful.

Chesebrough Pond's, a big manufacturer of toiletries and other consumer products, has big plans for robots. Its corporate research laboratory in Clinton, Connecticut, has developed a vision module that could be useful in giving factory robots sense. The company thinks there are 200 types of jobs in its factories around the world which people now do but which robots could take over. The tasks constitute anything between stacking shampoo bottles onto a transport system to inspecting labels. 'Consider all our employees who transfer objects on and off conveyors,' says Ray Davies, the head of the company's laboratories. 'If the technology develops as we hope, the robots could do ten per cent of these jobs by 1986.'

'Seeing' robots could also be useful in two key industries, aerospace and semiconductors. In both, there are many intricate jobs now done by people which the new machines could take over. Even more important, both industries comprise successful firms that are growing rapidly; it is this kind of company that has the money to spend on new and exotic technologies.

In aerospace, Lockheed, one of the world's biggest aeroplane manufacturers, has a research programme in 'seeing' robots. The company wants to use robots to drill and rivet aircraft assemblies – for instance to hold together parts of wings.

In the electronics industry, several firms around the world are trying to develop robots that will automatically put together electronic sub-assemblies or insert components onto printed circuit boards. In the second job, there are already many mechanisms that will fit such parts – for instance chips, capacitors or resistors – but which are unprogrammable. Thus they are no good to manufacturers who wish to make lots of changes in their product lines to meet fluctuations in demand. GEC-Marconi in the UK is one of the firms trying to develop a robot for this area. The firm is collaborating with the University of Hull which has built up expertise in robot vision. The partnership is one of several that have followed from a welcome, though rather late, £2.5 million plan announced in 1980 by the Science and Engineering Research Council to encourage a joint approach by academe and industry in the development of 'second generation' robots.

But it is in Japan where the most promising research is taking place. In the microchip industry, the firm NEC is already placing electronic components onto printed circuit boards with robots aided by TV cameras. The cameras also inspect the finished products to ensure that they are not defective. Fujitsu Fanuc is another company that is working on vision robots for assembly.

As though to emphasise that vision robots are not the only machines with sense, a third firm, Hitachi, had a very good start in the area of robots that can sense by feeling. The company developed what it calls its Hi-T-Hand, a gripper with a sense of touch, back in the early 1970s. The robot could do jobs such as fitting together parts of a motor by sliding one within another to give a close fit but in such a way that the components do not jam. (Another research organisation that has come up with a device that does a similar job is the Charles Stark Draper Laboratory. This developed a remote centre compliance for easing parts into others, for instance, putting a rod inside a close-fitting ring.)

In the 1980s, Hitachi is extremely keen on robots with sense, not just touch but vision too. It thinks that the new robots will play the biggest role in assembly work. The company analysed work at seventeen of its plants and found that assembly jobs accounted for thrity-five per cent of its employees' working hours. With the new 'sensing' machines, the company wants to eliminate seventy per cent of its (human) assembly workers within the next few years. By the end of the 1980s, the company thinks that factories could be run virtually completely by white collar staff with shop floor workers no longer required. The company has put its money where its mouth is. In 1981, it marshalled 500 of the company's top technicians to work on the new generation of robots, which it sees as playing a crucial part in boosting factory productivity in the late 1980s.

The Japan Industrial Robot Association has listed more than one hundred products which now have to be assembled by people but which, it says, could be left to robots if advances in technology continue at the current pace. The products include a great range of mass-produced items – typewriters, calculating machines, refrigerators, fire extinguishers, washing machines and so on – which at present require people in the assembly stage, if not in other manufacturing phases where the jobs are straightforward enough to be left to machines. If, today, assembly is the last bastion of the shop-floor worker while all the other jobs are being automated out of sight . . . this is likely not to be the case for much longer.

Japanese firms are extraordinarily imaginative about thinking up uses for 'second generation' robots. Mitsubishi is making a vision system similar to those which control the new kinds of robots. The system inspects fish or vegetables such as cucumbers in warehouses to see if they are fresh. The equipment is accurate enough to scan the items and divide the produce into several grades depending on their degree of wholesomeness. Toda Construction Company, one of Japan's five biggest building companies, plans to develop advanced robots to work on construction sites. The machines would walk around difficult terrain with artificial eyes to help them. According to the company, they would be especially useful in dangerous jobs such as dismantling disused nuclear power stations.

Even more imaginative is Automax of Tokyo which plans to build a cleaning robot for sweeping up homes and offices. The machine would have a little broom to do its job and would include a tactile sensor so that it knows when it bumps into walls. In this way it would negotiate its way round obstacles. The robot would have vision and sound sensors so that if it hears an unusual noise it would set off an alarm. The machine would thus act not only as a cleaner but as a night-watchman.

Fujitsu has plans for a 'secretary robot' that would write letters and apply official stamps, just as though a person was doing the job. And Tokyo's Waseda University is working on perhaps the most remarkable robot yet – a machine which works in hospitals which has touch sensors on its 'hands' so it can examine the human body. The machine has twenty-five 'fingers' whose tactile feelings are relayed to a central computer which makes sense of the information and decides on a diagnosis. According to the university, the machine would be specially good at feeling women's breasts in efforts to find lumps and give an early warning of breast cancer.

With all these strange – some might say fanciful – robots under development it is perhaps only too easy to get carried away and decide that the day of the 'seeing', 'feeling' robot is truly at hand. But it isn't – not for a few years anyway. In factories it is nowadays still easier and cheaper to employ ordinary human beings to do the kind of jobs for which the 'seeing' robots are becoming suitable. The cost and sophistication of the robots make them ill-fitted for most factories, many of which are more used to the ways of the 19th rather than the 20th century and which do not like to take on new ideas too fast. 'Seeing' robots for assembly, one of the most promising application areas, are still not tried and tested, at least not in the eyes of the people who run factories. In the sobering words of a 1981 Creative Strategies International market-research report on factory automation, there are no 'qualified products' in the area of robots for factory assembly. But this situation will change – quickly – as the robots get cheaper and cleverer, and, just as important, as factory workforces become more expensive.

Advances in other areas of machinery, not just robots, are contributing to this change. Factory engineers are realising that for robots and other devices to work effectively, they must be linked together. So instead of looking at just one small part of the total system they are considering the best way of putting together a complete factory that runs without people. The advances that this attitude engenders are bringing closer the era of the unmanned factory.

Chapter Ten
Tomorrow's factory

It is time to recapitulate. Manufacturing industry can be split into two broad classes, depending on whether it produces materials – steel and synthetic rubber for instance – or discrete items such as cars and washing machines. In the first category can be placed chemical works, glue factories and steel mills. Such industries operate predominantly by influencing chemical changes in materials that are liquids, for example by controlling temperatures and pressures.

Many functions in this kind of operation were fairly easy to automate twenty or thirty years ago. Visit a chemical works or a food-processing factory and you will spot few people bending over vats to dip in thermometers to check how fast reactions are proceeding. Distinctly thin on the ground will be workers who are physically opening valves or tipping flasks of liquid from one container to another. These jobs are nearly all done by machines which evolved during the first era of automation, what this book calls the third industrial revolution, during the 1950s.

The second class of manufacturing industry – the one in which this book is mainly interested – is more concerned with physical changes in solids. The agents of change in this group are mechanical tools, with which people bend, batter, cut, plane, drill, shape and weave pieces of metal, plastic, wood and fibre. The clash of steel against steel or iron against wood – these are typical, not to say dominant, activities in the great mass of industries that produce discrete items. The products themselves can vary enormously; they can be anything from furniture to microchips, tin-openers to machine tools, shoes to bazooka shells.

The mechanical implements used in this class of manufacturing operations are predominantly machine tools. These cut, drill or otherwise shape pieces of solid, under the control of a human operator or, in the more advanced cases, of a computer. The importance in manufacturing industry of machining is difficult to over-stress. If you consider the 18 classes of products for which, according to the EEC, world demand is growing at the greatest rate, 12 of them include items whose production processes demand at least some machining (Table 2).

Machining has, however, always presented manufacturers with problems. Although there have been many advances, both in the shaping implements of machine tools and the mechanisms that

Table 2. Growth in volume of world domestic demand – manufactured products

Product	Annual growth rate (%)	Machining used in production
Office machinery, data processing	13·4	√
Plastic products	12·5	√
Electronic components	12·3	√
Optical instruments and cameras	11·6	√
Basic organic chemistry	11·4	×
Plastics, artificial fibres	11·4	×
Warehouse/building equipment	10·2	×
Watches and clocks	9·6	√
Knitted goods	9·5	×
Machinery for specialised industries	9·3	√
Electrical equipment	9·1	√
Pharmaceuticals	9·0	×
Engines, turbines, pumps	8·5	√
Consumer electronics	8·4	√
Machine tools	8·3	√
Domestic electric appliances	8·2	√
Heavy boilers	8·2	√
Paints and dyes	7·9	×

Source: *The Old World and the New Technologies* by Michel Godet and Olivier Ruyssen

control them, most factories have found it difficult to machine items in an automated fashion, without people being present. So this put a brake for many years on the idea of the automated machining line. The engineering, or metal-bashing, industries in which machining is important were largely unaffected by the automation of the 1950s and 1960s. This is why, if you go to a typical factory representing this kind of industry, there will still be plenty of people around.

In such plants, if a piece of metal has to be cut or drilled, then someone has to do it, albeit with machinery of a sophistication that, one hundred and fifty years ago, would have been difficult to imagine. If bits of material have to be welded, then the responsibility belongs to a person not a machine. When a job calls for items to be joined – for instance in the assembly of a car or a washing machine, a mechanism can do the task nowhere near as well as human fingers. In a complex manufacturing operation, which involves a sequence of jobs to make a product whose design will probably change from one week to the next on account of switches in customer taste, people are even more vital. The task of transferring items between the different stages of a manufacturing operation is too difficult to be left totally to a machine. This is even if, in such transport operations, a mechanism aids the human worker – as happens, of course, when someone moves lumps of metal with a fork-lift truck.

All this, at any rate, used to be the case. But, little by little, the world of manufacturing is changing. In many of today's metal-bashing industries, machines are getting better at doing some of the tasks that, a few years ago, were indisputably the preserve of humans.

Robots, as we have seen, are specially important as the programmable mechanisms that can do a lot of the handling jobs which, previously, were difficult to automate. Thus they can play a part in welding, spraying paint or stacking objects on top of each other. At the same time, they are useful in transferring goods between different stages of manufacturing operations.

In these operations, the machines that shape parts are coming under the control of ever more sophisticated computers that permit two things. First, they make it possible to fabricate goods automatically, with few people involved. Secondly, one set of automatic hardware can make a range of different goods, depending on the way the equipment is programmed. This gives the manufacturer the flexibility that, previously, he could never get from machines. Most automated factory machinery, transfer line or automatic paint-spray equipment for instance, works only for one kind of job; this forces manufacturers to use, in so many production processes, people – who are wonderfully flexible yet expensive. When their versatility begins to be rivalled by machines, however, it is time for people to get out of the way and let the machines take over. This, in many industries, is what will soon start to happen.

In most engineering firms, there are three basic operations. First, workers have to decide what kind of product they want – this is the process of design. Next, the agreed items have to be produced; this is where the shop floor enters the picture, with its various production processes such as machining, assembly, testing and handling. Finally, there is an essential amount of administration, in which people keep records concerning customers' orders; stock levels; goods entering and leaving the factory; the amount of work taking place; and data about employees, for instance, who is off sick and how much workers are being paid.

In the engineering industry of the future, all three of these basic operations will be done with the help of computers, which will greatly reduce the need for labour. In design, engineers are already using computers to draw products and to work out how they will be made.

In this activity, a draughtsman sits in front of a computer terminal, which has a keyboard and a display screen, as in a TV set. He types in instructions about the part he wants to draw, for instance, its function and what he wants it to look like. Depending on the keys he presses, lines appear on the screen until gradually a complex part – for instance a piece of a gear assembly – appears in outline on the screen. Drawings of small segments of the product that the draughtsman does not want to build up from scratch can be instantly transferred to the screen; the worker does this by pressing more keys to call up from a computer the description of the part in which he is interested. Then the draughtsman's completed drawing can be stored, along with thousands of others, in the memory cells of the same computer, which is connected to the terminal by cable.

Computerised design equipment can increase the productivity of a draughtsman by five times or more. With the old manual method, he has to draw out his design laboriously with a pencil and paper; if he wants to change the drawing, he either has to rub bits out or scrap the whole thing and start again. With the new technique, on the other hand, the worker can change small parts of his creation just by pressing the buttons on his keyboard; and by using data stored in the computer, he can call on other people's work to add vital bits to the design. Further, it is an easy job to compare the drawing with others, perhaps of related products; this is done by flashing the two in sequence onto the screen. The new kind of computerised design equipment makes it improbable that we shall see an increased demand for draughtsmen in the factories of the 1980s and 1990s.

What about administration? In most factories, a plethora of people in different offices keep track of the huge amount of information that ensures their plants function properly. As a rule, the information is kept in manual files or, alternatively, in separate computers. Increasingly, however, the computers concerned with different administrative tasks are being interlinked, which makes it easier to run the factory efficiently.

In a firm that makes things, administration is all about the products that the factory floor is putting together. So it makes sense to link up the administrative computers with the computers that run the manufacturing operations. In a modern car factory, for instance, staff in a control room will feed information about customers' orders and stock deliveries into a computer which is directly linked to the machines on the shop floor. The computer will analyse the information and decide how much work each of the machines should be doing.

One of the most advanced computer systems for factories is in a £32 million plant run by Leyland Vehicles in Lancashire. The plant, which makes trucks, contains seven computers. These record customers' orders, defects in finished vehicles, and the results of tests on engines. With the terminals, which are scattered throughout offices and the factory floor itself, staff can find out, for instance, whether customers have come up with new demands for modifications in the trucks they are buying, or if the factory is running out of components such as wheels. This helps people both on the shop floor and in offices to plan more efficiently. The computer system even records the number of workers who have turned up on a particular day – all employees have to 'sign in' with the computer by pressing buttons on a terminal – and is linked to an automated warehouse. In the latter, small microprocessor-controlled trolleys automatically fetch parts from storage racks according to instructions from the central computer network.

The dream of factory engineers all over the world is to link up the computer systems for design and administration with the ones controlling factory production. Before considering how this is done, let us examine what is taking place to make manufacturing processes themselves more efficient.

Work is already well advanced on designing computer-controlled production cells. Here, a workshop would have several machine tools, each with its own range of tools in a bandolier from which it can automatically pick an implement for a specified job: in this way a machine can work for (say) half-an-hour with a cutting mechanism, then switch over to drill a hole in another piece of metal. The instructions that tell such a machine how to operate – for instance which tool to pluck from the bandolier and then how to use it – are normally lodged in a microcomputer that forms part of the equipment's control mechanism. In most factories that use these so-called numerically-controlled machine tools – the phrase was introduced in Chapter 6 – a human is responsible for giving the machine its instructions. He also has to stand by to adjust the hardware while it operates. But in the new concept of the production cell, the operator's job is done by another computer, a highly-ranked supervisory machine whose role is similar to the foreman in a factory run by humans.

Such a 'supervisor' computer could control anything up to ten or twenty individual machines. It sends instructions to them in much the same way as a human overseer first formulates a strategy for getting jobs done and then tells other people to actually do the work. In engineer's jargon, such production cells of machines controlled by other machines are called direct-numerically controlled systems. Japan has been a leader in using such equipment. In 1977, that country contained eighty direct-numerically controlled systems while Britain could boast only three.

With these systems, there is less work for people. A separate operator for each computerised machine tool is no longer required. Now a conventional, that is stand-alone, computerised or NC tool can do something like five times as much work in the same time as an old-fashioned, manually-controlled machine in which a person has to guide the mechanism through every stage of its fashioning actions. So with perhaps one operator for three machines in the new, direct-numerically controlled system, the output for each operator is increased by a factor of something like fifteen, compared with the old way of making things. The production cells still, however, need someone to feed instructions to the central 'master' computer. They require workers to scurry from one machine to another to load raw bits of metal and take off finished products.

But efficiency can be increased even further with a second type of production system that has appeared in the past few years. In this equipment, a central computer not only controls each separate machine tool under its charge; it also arranges for the blocks of metal being machined to travel from one tool to another by some transport mechanism. The latter can vary according to taste. It can be a conveyor belt that carries parts around the system; it can be a sequence of robots that grab the components and place them in the relevant machine tool at the appropriate moment; or, most imaginatively, the transport equipment could comprise a series of unmanned trolleys that trundle around the factory floor and bear a load of raw parts from one point to another. The transport concept immediately cuts out the need for workers who put the components in place on the various machines.

The key factor of these systems is their flexibility. Not only does the supervisory computer tell the machines under it to execute a wide range of functions; it also directs the transport mechanism to carry parts round the system in whatever manner the computer decides is most efficient. Thus in a system comprising machines A to D, the central computer could ensure that a part due for a series of

Fig. 5: Evolution of computerised manufacturing systems

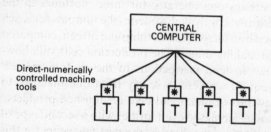

Manually controlled machine tool

Numerically controlled machine tool (with own microcomputer)

Direct-numerically controlled machine tools

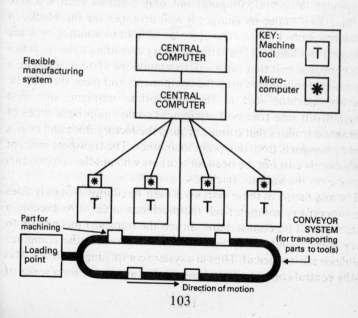

Flexible manufacturing system

KEY:
Machine tool

Micro-computer

CENTRAL COMPUTER

CENTRAL COMPUTER
CENTRAL COMPUTER

Part for machining

Loading point

CONVEYOR SYSTEM (for transporting parts to tools)

Direction of motion

complex machining operations visits first A, then C, before going back to B and on to D. At each point on the tour around the system, the part would be machined in a different way until it emerges as a finished product. The next component that enters the system could then travel in an entirely different sequence. You can now appreciate the difference between this method of making things, and the inflexible automation of the transfer line, where there is no chance of varying the set sequence in which parts travel through the system: it is A to B to C to D, or nothing at all. The new equipment had to have a name; and engineers have coined for it the title 'flexible manufacturing system' – uninspiring but factual enough. Figure 5 shows a typical design, together with an indication of how the hardware has evolved from earlier machining systems.

Operating one of the new systems is not too difficult. An engineer sits in a control room with a keyboard-equipped terminal and probably two computers – one each to control the transport mechanism and the machine tools themselves. He types into a terminal the details of the parts he wants made, and when is the deadline for making them. The job of scheduling the work between the various machines in the system is then left to the two computers.

How well they do this job depends very much on the quality of the internal software in the machines. This software is the set of basic operating instructions that has been drawn up by the system's suppliers. Now this job definitely is labour intensive; at present anyway, computer software cannot be written by machines. In the case of an advanced flexible manufacturing system announced in 1980 by Cincinnati Milacron, writing the internal software took an effort equivalent to thirty-five man-years. But once written it can be used time after time – on all the machines of its type that Cincinnati Milacron sells.

Flexible manufacturing systems are expensive. A system with six machining stations costs about £5 million. But they bring four main benefits that start to justify the cost. First, they require fewer people, so saving wage costs. A four-station system would need just two or three people; they would look after the computers, maintain the system; and load and unload parts onto the transport mechanism at a special loading area. This operating staff can be compared with the twenty or so who would produce the same output with a series of manually-controlled machine tools.

Secondly, the new equipment saves space. It is much more compact than the old spread-out arrangement of separate machine tools which clutter up a factory and require forklift trucks and the like to pass up and down between them. According to studies at the University of Berlin, a flexible manufacturing system can be expected to take up sixty per cent of the space of an equivalent set of orthodox tools. So firms could anticipate selling off parts of their factories – that is unless they start producing more goods – if they change over from the old to the new method of making things.

The third advantage is that with the new equipment organisations can react much more quickly to changes in demand for their products. Most factories that produce goods in small batches use collections of old-fashioned machine tools. Because of the number of machining stages involved, making a new object from scratch takes a long time. So if a customer comes up with a new order – perhaps he or she wants a casing for an electric motor that, for instance, is slightly bigger than normal – the manufacturer laboriously has to take a lump of metal through the necessary machining operations using several tools spread around the factory. This can take days, if not weeks. With the new system, however, the owner would simply press a few buttons on his computer console to modify the way that the equipment operates; and, hey presto, his trusty supervisory computers would see that the modification is made. The finished product would emerge from the system a few hours later.

The final benefit from the new kind of hardware is that machines can often make complicated things more accurately than people. This may sound like sacrilege; but in a manufacturing operation, humans lose concentration and get tired and therefore make mistakes. A machine – once it is working properly, is well programmed and is kept in good repair – does none of these things.

The business of making, and owning, flexible manufacturing systems is still in its infancy. In 1980 the world contained somewhere between 50 and 100 such pieces of equipment. Roughly half were in Japan; the rest were divided between the US and Europe; the Communist bloc accounted for a large proportion. To date, the systems have been used mainly to make variations on one kind of product. In other words you will have trouble finding equipment that can turn out, say, pieces for engine blocks at the same time as bits of electric motors or threshing blades for combine harvesters. But in due course, there seems no reason to doubt that flexible manufacturing systems will be truly flexible and turn out a complete range of objects depending on the programs in the central computers.

The biggest makers of flexible systems are in the US and Japan. Cincinnati Milacron, Kearney and Trecker, Hitachi and Kawasaki are among the leading firms. Flexible systems around the world make anything from razors to parts for military tanks and turbine blades.

Rockwell, for instance, has a plant in Newark, Ohio, which makes different kinds of axle units for trucks with a seven-station system. Ingersoll Rand has another which turns out motor cases; Yamatake Honeywell makes twenty different kinds of valve with one of its systems in Japan.

Britain, by contrast, has taken a back seat in developments in flexible manufacturing systems. This was despite the ironic fact that the UK took an early lead in this equipment. In the late 1960s, Molins, which produces cigarette-making machinery, brought out a (then) revolutionary machine tool called System 24. It was an ambitious automated machine designed to make small-batch production as efficient as long-run production. As such, it was a forerunner of many of today's flexible systems.

But System 24 ate up huge amounts of development cash. Although the hardware was sold to a few important customers – Rolls-Royce, Texas Instruments and IBM for instance – Molins could not recover its costs. System 24 pushed the company £500,000 into the red in 1970. And in 1973, Molins closed down its whole machine tool division with a total loss of £5 million.

It was another story of a major British invention which eventually failed, leaving manufacturers overseas to take up the idea and cash in on it. Poor marketing and lack of enthusiasm among UK manufacturers for advanced equipment were to blame.

In Britain, firms are still reluctant to chance their arm with flexible systems. This is despite entreaties from the government and leading engineers that experience in the systems would help to safeguard the future of manufacturing industry in Britain. By mid 1981, there was still no firm in the UK which had a fully operating flexible manufacturing system. Two companies, however, had made a start. Normalair-Garrett was building a system to make aerospace parts at a factory in Crewkerne, Somerset; and the 600 Group had begun to construct an experimental system to turn out parts for machine tools. Both projects were being helped by grants from the Department of Industry under what it calls its Automated Small-batch Production project. Progress was a lot slower than it would have liked, however; few people came forward from industry to make a grab for the money being offered. In 1982, however, prospects began to look better. Several more firms got involved with the DOI's project. And GEC, Britain's biggest electrical manufacturer, set up a new division with 250 people to engineer and install the new flexible systems.

In contrast with the UK, engineers in Japan are rushing ahead with flexible manufacturing systems. The country was the site of one of the world's first examples of such equipment. Since it started work in 1972, the hardware, run by Yanmar Diesel at its factory near Osaka, has churned out thousands of cylinder heads for engines. The equipment needs just one person to turn out products that, with conventional equipment, would require a staff of fifteen.

An indication of what lies ahead comes from a plant owned by Fujitsu Fanuc, one of Japan's biggest industrial machinery companies, in the foothills of Mount Fuji near Tokyo. The factory contains several kinds of machine tool, a battery of robots, an automated warehouse from which materials are unloaded on little trolleys, and a small army of unmanned carts that glide around the floor between the various machines. The factory is certainly not 'unmanned'; when it is fully operational, according to the company, the factory will require one hundred and fifty people – plus a full complement of thirty robots for handling tasks. But the plant will have a prodigious output; Fujitsu Fanuc says it will make each month five hundred industrial machines such as lathes, plus three hundred and fifty new robots. The robots in the factory are employed mainly for loading parts into machine tools; so the day is not yet here when robots directly assemble other robots. (For news of how this might occur, see Chapter 14). Just to emphasise that their plant still depends on humans, the company's officials have built at the factory houses for thirty of the workers' families, plus a sixty-room dormitory for visitors. Presumably the company feels it will get better results from its workers if it stops them going too far to their houses in the evening.

In terms of advanced equipment, however, the Fujitsu Fanuc plant is small beer compared with another plant under construction in Japan. This £26 million factory, which should be finished by 1983, is being put together at the state-owned Mechanical Engineering Laboratory at Tskuba City just outside Tokyo. Few Westerners are allowed inside to see what is going on. Just to deter unauthorised sightseers, security guards surround the section of the laboratory where engineers are building the plant.

The driving force behind the project is the obvious enough idea that machining – what happens in flexible manufacturing systems – is only one part, albeit an important one, of the overall production

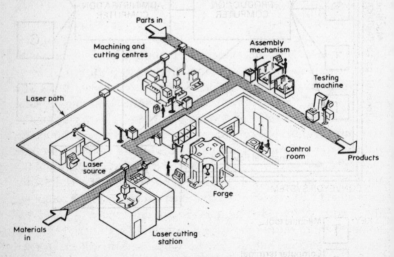

Fig. 6: Plan for Japan's advanced factory
This diagram first appeared in New Scientist, 30 October, 1980

process in engineering workshops. Therefore, officials at Japan's Ministry of International Trade and Industry, which is paying for the factory, want to link a flexible manufacturing system with a number of other factory operations. If all goes to plan, the plant will contain machine tools for drilling, cutting and otherwise fashioning

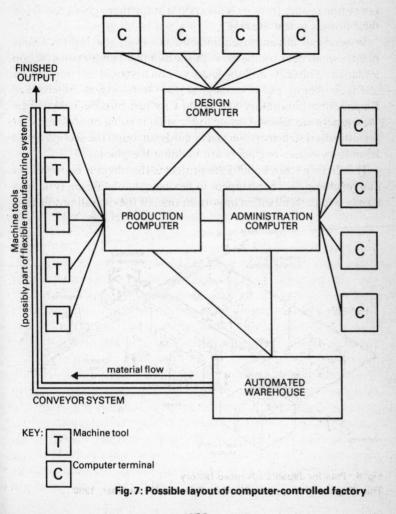

Fig. 7: Possible layout of computer-controlled factory

109

bits of metal; assembly stations where robots will put things together; a forge that makes lumps of metal of a standard shape that are later machined; and a series of special machines which cut metal with high-powered lasers. There will also be testing modules – TV cameras linked to computers past which goods flow on conveyors for inspection. Robots and conveyor belts will transfer parts between the different parts of the factory so there will be few humans needed for the routine tasks of humping metal around. The whole operation will be co-ordinated by computers that control the flow of materials around the factory. When complete the factory should look something like Figure 6.

According to one proposal, the components of the machinery in the plant will be built from standard modules. Workers will then be able to take machines apart on the shop floor and re-assemble the bits to make different ones, rather like making models of Lego. This should increase the flexibility of the operation. According to the Japanese government, the plant will serve as a model for engineers around the country. They will be able to visit it and pick up hints about how to build their own advanced factories. Crucially, many of the country's top engineering firms are building components of the new factory and so are picking up valuable experience in the advanced technologies involved.

The Japanese are leaping ahead in controlling production processes – the metal-bashing and assembly operations of the automated factory – but they do not seem so enthusiastic about co-ordinating the other essential parts as well. I am referring to the engineer's dream of linking design, administration and production in one computer-controlled operation. In this area, the US is doing the most work.

American engineers have as their goal a factory that in diagrammatic form is represented by Figure 7. There are three main computers; one each for the flexible manufacturing system, design and administration. Instructions that enter the first computer control how and which goods are made; draughtsmen work out which goods they *want* made with the second machine; and in the third are lodged all the details about orders, scheduling, the state of stocks and so on. All three computers are linked to each other; and also to an automated warehouse from which raw materials are passed by a transport mechanism to the factory floor and the machining area. In their wilder moments, the engineers also dream of adding assembly and testing stations in the manner of the Japanese project at Tskuba City.

The few places where humans would get directly involved with the factory's processes would be predominantly in the design room and in a control area where the factory's administrators sit. Draughtsmen would design products using their keyboards and screens; the codes representing these parts would flash along wires to the production computer; which, in turn, would instruct its battery of machine tools to get weaving and make the items. Just for good measure, the computer would also see that bits and pieces are put together in the way that the humans running the show expect; there would be a few 'seeing' robots scattered about the production department to make the assembly job easier. Meanwhile, the factory's administrators would keep track of the whole operation, getting information from the system by keying in instructions to their terminals. For instance, they could find out if there are sufficient stocks to make a specified product; they could find out when machines break down and despatch repair men (for these people would still be vital) to right matters.

At the heart of the factory would be a communications network of amazing complexity that links all the machines in the plant so that they constantly relay instructions to each other. In this way all the machines in the plant would keep each other informed of what is going on. A robot would be always waiting to grab a chunk of metal as it comes its way; a machine tool would stand ready with the right tool and the correct assortment of instructions as a part is slid in front of it for shaping. 'Be prepared' is the maxim for the machines in the factory of the future. It is not surprising that some of the engineers working on these entities are experts in telecommunications; the mechanisms in the plants will be linked by wires in much the same way as the telephone network connects up towns and villages, houses and offices in the more familiar human world outside. The main difference is that the machines will talk to each other in a binary code which humans find unintelligble.

111

This kind of operation would require just a fraction of the people that a typical factory now employs. It would not be an unmanned factory, but it would be pretty near such a thing. Given the rate of technical progress over the past ten to twenty years, such plants will be with us by the end of the century. Already, the US market for computerised factory equipment is estimated to be growing at a rate of forty-four per cent per year. By 1984, $2,200 million worth of computer-aided design and manufacturing hardware should be sold in the US – about four times as much as in 1980 (see Table 3).

Appropriately enough – for it is computers that promise to make these factories possible – the most highly automated plants at present make semiconductors, the tiny chips of silicon which are computers' building blocks. In such factories, engineers first design chips with computerised techniques; after a long spell at the keyboard and screen, the characteristics of the chips that they want are lodged in a computer. This code then passes directly to a machine which, with electron beams, 'prints' microscopic patterns on thin slices of silicon. The pattern is so dense that the lines on it are perhaps two micrometres apart, where one micrometre is a millionth of a metre. Together with other, less densely-packed patterns which have been defined with visible light (similar to the printing process used in photography), the lines mark the positions on chips of tiny blobs of material which, when they are put in place, are responsible for these devices' electronic properties. To position the 'blobs', the pieces of silicon, once 'printed', pass between different chemical and physi al processes which are highly automated. The silicon slices are rarely handled by people; they pass either on conveyor belts or on layers of air. The whole operation is co-ordinated by a computer. When the production process is over, the silicon is dissected into lots of tiny chips, which could be microprocessors, memories, or other electronic devices. These then have to be tested and packed into small plastic containers that include interconnections to other bits of electrical apparatus. Once again, these operations are increasingly done under the control of computers; in at least one assembly system operated by NEC of Japan, a 'seeing' robot helps to guide the chips into their packaging.

Already, chips are being made with this production method; it

112

Table 3. The estimated market for computer-aided design and computer-aided manufacturing equipment in US$m. Source: Merrill Lynch

	1978 $	Growth %	1979 $	Growth %	1980 $	Growth %	1981 $	Growth %	1984 $	1980–84 annual growth %
Mechanical	65	+60	120	+85	199	+66	310	+56	1,100	53
Electronic	49	+36	90	+84	149	+66	215	+45	396	28
Civil engineering	25	+50	50	+100	75	+50	108	+45	308	42
Mapping	15	+70	30	+100	75	+133	105	+45	242	37
Other	11	+60	20	+82	17	− 15	27	+59	154	73
TOTAL	$165	+60	$310	+88	$510	+65	$765	+50	$2,200	44

won't be long before the same type of treatment is extended to other products.

General Electric, the giant American firm that makes all sorts of electrical equipment, has certainly made a stride in this direction. It has purchased a firm called Calma that makes computerised design equipment; and it plans to use in its factories, and sell to outsiders, Italian-designed assembly robots called Pragmas. General Electric thinks that, eventually, all the individual parts of a computerised factory could be linked up; design, machining and assembly would all be co-ordinated. As a final move, the company is developing voice-recognition equipment for robots so that people can talk to their machines to tell them what to do. The day of the moving, feeling, seeing – and hearing – robot would then be at hand, and the machines would do a mightily useful job in the world's factories. But this would make robots 'intelligent' . . . almost like people. And they could never be that . . . or could they?

PART 4

The Robot Future

Chapter Eleven
Machines that think: artificial intelligence

Can computers think? If they can, it may be possible to build truly intelligent robots that operate like humans, along the lines of the machines that appeared in Capek's play *R.U.R.*

Few issues stir up a more passionate debate, not only among scientists and engineers but among men and women from all walks of life. People are fascinated by the notion that machines can be somehow more than inanimate objects and have personalities, life-styles even, of their own. On one hand, such machines could be extremely useful – in industry and in lots of other places. Even now, some people claim special relationships with machinery. Ships, cars, even humble items such as cookers and lathes: all have been doted on in their time. So machines that you can talk to, understand and perhaps even love, would be certain to have their admirers.

There is an opposing view, however. The human consciousness shows a deep distaste for the thought that objects apart from people or other animals can have intelligence. If this is indeed the case, people aren't so special after all. The supposedly unique thing about humans – that they possess a spirit which confers on them characteristics above everything else in the world – suddenly does not count for very much. Even though people sometimes have problems with machinery (when it displaces them from work for instance) they can rub along with it, as long as they know that they are the cleverer. Could men and women cope with machines that are smarter than they are?

The discipline in which scientists try to give machines the characteristics of humans is called artificial intelligence, or A.I. Nils Nilsson, a noted American researcher, sums up the concept in his 1980 book *Principles of Artificial Intelligence:* 'Many human activities, such as writing computer programs, doing mathematics, engaging in commonsense reading, understanding language, and even driving

117

an automobile are said to demand "intelligence". Over the past few decades, several computer systems have been built that can perform tasks such as these . . . We might say that such systems possess some degree of artificial intelligence.'

The question of whether computers can think is better phrased another way. Thinking in humans entails a reordering of thoughts – which, physiologically, are electric pulses that flash through the brain – due to the influence of three factors. These are previous experiences, hereditary 'programming' and new, external and internal stimuli relayed to and from the brain by the nervous system. The original question now becomes: 'Can computers rearrange the electrical codes contained in their memories according to a combination of data that are already programmed into them, plus information relayed to them through sensors about external events?' And the answer is – 'Yes, they can.'

Patrick Winston, a researcher at the Massachusetts Institute of Technology, discusses the debate about 'thinking' machines in his book *Artificial Intelligence*. 'Intelligent computers do not organise themselves out of nothing, so in some uninteresting sense their abilities descend from human programmers. But it is equally true that humans are indebted to the genetic code. Somehow there must be enough innate information-processing power to get beyond the threshold above which learning from the environment takes place. Once humans bring computer intelligence up to this level, computers will no doubt augment their directly programmed gifts by the same means humans do: by being told, by reading, by asking questions, by being curious and so on.'

Winston, then, is looking forward to the day when computers are not content with getting all their instructions and experiences indirectly from humans, but start to find out these things for themselves. At this point, we will have truly intelligent or 'thinking' machines.

What relevance has this to robots and to the whole question of automation? All the devices that this book has considered include three main elements: a power source, a mechanical component that moves or otherwise does something and a control unit. In robots and the other new factory tools, the computerised control unit is the most important element: how the equipment moves or how it is

118

powered is nothing particularly revolutionary. So anything that changes the way computers operate, to make them more intelligent, will have a big effect on robots.

At present, it is very difficult to get computers to rearrange the data in their memories in a way similar to human thinking. The main problem is the way in which the machines are designed. They are used to accepting large quantities of information and processing it in a set manner according to a rigid set of instructions contained in a program. If computers are asked to do something which it is impossible to put into a programming language, then they cannot do it.

As a corollary of this, it is difficult for people to ask computers questions, talk to them, and make them understand even simple statements. The only way to do this is to frame the communication in terms of a special programming language, which translates human requests into a form the computer can understand. But the mechanics of translation, as well as making the whole job more complex, cuts down on the range of commands that a human can put to a machine.

The job of researchers in artificial intelligence, then, is to give computers what amounts to common sense. They must be given sensors by which they can pick up information from their surroundings; but, more importantly, the machines must be able to make sense of this information in a far more powerful way than today's computers. The devices must be given the reasoning power, and the intuition, approaching that of the human brain.

Computers that work like this would have two main effects. First, they would be much easier to use as people could communicate with them in a normal manner – by speaking ordinary sentences for instance. Secondly, the power of the computer to work out problems for itself would be increased tremendously.

Although the US and, to a lesser extent, Britain are the leaders in artificial-intelligence work that could produce such computers, Japan is showing every sign of wanting to muscle in. Crucially, its government and business leaders have realised far better than their Western counterparts the importance of giving computers intelligence. Through the Ministry of International Trade and Industry, the government is likely to spend some £200 million during the

1980s on developing a brand new generation of computer that is completely intelligent. This, the Ministry thinks, could bring Japan world dominance in virtually every area concerned with electronics and data processing.

In a remarkable document released in 1980, the Japan Information-tion Processing Development Centre, an organisation funded by both government and industry, spells out what it would like to see the country achieve in computers by 1990: 'In order to increase the intelligence of computers and make them a more amenable partner for people, it is necessary to somehow provide computers with knowledge related to the particular field of application, and the techniques to apply this knowledge. At the same time it must have other faculties – such as powers of association and inference, and the ability to learn.'

The document's authors concisely pinpoint the difficulties about present-day computers: 'There is too great a gap between the knowledge which any man is expected to possess (common sense) and the knowledge possessed by a computer system. Thus, in com-municating with a computer, it is necessary to give detailed instruc-tions about things which, if one were communicating with another man, one would be able to rely on the other party to use his judgement about. In order to overcome this problem, what is required is, in a word, a computer system with common sense. Ideally, such a system would be able to draw related items from its knowledge base in making judgements concerning matters which it had not been given instructions about.'

Japan's new computer, which it calls a 'fifth generation' machine, would be quite different from today's models. The chief innovation is a 'knowledge information system', which contains an 'accumula-tion of knowledge that is effective and also general to users'. The Japanese say the knowledge system would contain three kinds of information: general knowledge that mainly relates to understand-ing natural (i.e. human) languages, 'system' knowledge that makes the computer work properly and an 'expert knowledge base' con-taining the knowledge of human experts.

The Japanese plan is noteworthy not so much for the technical brilliance with which it describes the fifth generation computer. The proposals are not new; the Japanese have merely borrowed ideas worked out by A.I. researchers in the West. The main point is that the Japanese government has formulated a strategy for actually building such a machine. It wants to set up a full-time institute, to which the brightest of the country's computer engineers would be seconded. Their main aim is to construct a fifth generation machine by 1990. The computer – and advances in artificial intelligence in general – could have a big impact on industry, as the next chapter will show. The project indicates that, if the West is worried about Japan's growing dominance in manufacturing, the concern is better founded than most people think.

No-one doubts that building a 'thinking computer' will be extemely difficult. But given Japan's impressive advances in other areas of industry, the country will probably go at least part of the way to achieving its goal. The changes that this could usher in are awe-inspiring.

121

Chapter Twelve
Beyond automation

The last chapter considered how artificial intelligence will change the way computers operate. This one will examine how A.I. will make its mark on robots and manufacturing industry in general.

I have already discussed two basic kinds of robots. The first – which are the ones seen mostly today – are controlled by computers containing series of instructions for which a person is responsible. The person can change these instructions by re-programming his device. This gives a robot flexibility and this is why it is particularly useful in manufacturing.

In more advanced robots, considered in Chapter 9, the machines have sensors which pick up information from around them. On the basis of this knowledge, the robot's computer sends instructions to the machine's arms and grippers. The machines are therefore in touch with the world – in a way that the orthodox 'stupid' robots are not – and are able to adjust their performance according to events in that world. The mechanism by which they do this is 'feedback'.

But this feedback is not very advanced. By no stretch of the imagination could a robot with this mechanism be said to be 'thinking', even allowing for the imprecision with which this word is customarily used. The feedback robot does no more than what you or I do if we hit our heads on a low ceiling or if, when walking along a road, our eyes spot a lamp-post ahead. In both cases we take immediate action – we cry out or alter our gait – as a *reflex*. No thought is involved, in the sense that this entails a reformulation of policy.

A third order of robots can now be postulated. The new machines have higher-order feedback mechanisms, in which experiences and external events act on the devices in such a way that not just specific movements, but whole policies of behaviour, are regulated. This class of machines, in which the principles of artificial intelligence are

122

incorporated in their computerised control units, will exhibit 'policy feedback' – a term that Norbert Wiener used in his 1950s classic *The Human Use of Human Beings*, which is essential reading for anyone interested in the theory of machines.

If we consider the business of seeing, we can immediately appreciate the difference between the 'seeing' robots of Chapter 9 and the higher-order machines. A simple 'seeing' robot compares an image passed to it by a TV camera with other images stored in digital codes in its computer memory. Such a robot told to pick up, say, a pencil from a heap of stationery equipment will scan images of fountain pens, paper clips, writing paper and so on until it spots a long, thin object with a tapered end. A comparison of this image with the one in its memory then follows; as the two correlate, the robot realises it has struck gold and picks up the object.

The problem about these robots – and you might have realised this already – is that they can recognise only those items they have seen already. If for instance, the pencil does not have a pointed end because it is blunt, the robot would miss the object – unless it has been told in advance what to look for.

A robot with 'policy feedback' would be smarter. It would see a long, thin object, note its blunt end and deduce that this could be nothing other than a pencil – albeit in appearance slightly different from expected.

In a similar way, if a robot were asked to pick out a wine glass from a heap of crockery, a conventional machine would fail unless it had an exact image of this item in its memory. A higher-order robot would, however, work out – from stored images of, say, cups and beer mugs plus a general knowledge about receptacles for drink – that an object with a stem and a hollow end could be nothing other than a wine glass. The robot would emulate the way in which a person, who has plenty of experience about cups and beer mugs but for some reason has never come across a wine glass, would deduce the meaning of such an object.

Machines that can operate with intuition or by making deductions would be of obvious benefit in many areas, not least of them in factories. Such devices, provided they are mechanically able as well as brilliant thinkers, could walk around plants inspecting things.

They would do this not with the 'reflex' intelligence of ordinary computers but with the broad understanding and general knowledge of a person. They could make long-term policy decisions, for instance on investment or on the welfare of human workers.

The machines would be able to understand speech just like a person. People could talk to them when giving orders – or even hold conversations. 'How are you today, Machine No. 657X?' – 'Not so good; perhaps you would be so kind as to change the fuses in control-rack number seven.' This could be the kind of discourse that takes place in the factories of the future.

Before this chapter sounds too much like science fiction, let us return to the present day. How do people intend making such incredibly clever machines?

Admittedly, the theory of artificial intelligence is in better shape than practical systems. Intelligent, or higher-order robots, do not yet exist outside research laboratories. But in recent years, important advances have been made, mainly by researchers in the US. As we saw in the last chapter, the Japanese government is so enthusiastic about the theory of A.I. that it is committing a lot of money and resources to making the principle work. I will now consider in turn the various areas of A.I. that have relevance to robots and manufacturing industry in general.

The art of perception

To make a machine that perceives things like a person is a great ambition of A.I. workers. There are two stages in this work, each by no means easy. First the researcher has to find out, normally from work in psychology, the processes by which people visualise scenes. Then he has to translate these processes to a machine.

When someone looks at a scene, sensory information provided by the eyes flashes to the brain for analysis. This occurs not in the way of the simple 'seeing' robots of Chapter 9. These robots compare a store of images kept in the brain. For this to work for humans, however, the brain would have to keep on file millions upon millions of separate images just in case its owner ever encountered them. Apart from requiring a mammoth storage space, the process of comparing every object in a scene with memorised images would take far too long. Instead, the brain looks for lines, colours, shapes and patterns in the image and then, working incredibly quickly, builds up an understanding of what the objects in the picture are and what they do. It is likely, for instance, that when a person sees an oak standing in a field, his brain first records the object's colour, then the general shape, then the fact that it has leaves; and from this concludes that it is a tree. The fine-tuning of the description, providing the conclusion about what kind of tree it is, comes later.

To let a computer understand in this manner, we must feed into it a set of instructions that makes it analyse pictures in the way that a person does. So the computer looks for lines and so on; when it has built up a certain level of understanding, it must be able to check hypotheses about the objects in the picture. After a person's brain has spotted that a picture contains something green which is round at the top and long and thin at the bottom, it will not bother with more processing steps, which, for instance, look for horizontal lines or more colours that would simply waste time.

Instead, the brain will hypothesise that the object is a tree; to check this, it will look for leaves. If, indeed, the picture contains items that can be identified as such, the hypothesis is confirmed. A similar series of processing steps must take place for intelligent robots.

The brain of such a clever robot would contain a tremendous amount of information about what it can expect to encounter in specific circumstances. But the machine works in a structured way to use this information as efficiently as possible. For example, after working out that an object in front of it is a tree, it would then check for other items nearby that correspond with things that it expects to find near trees. The robot's computer would activate processes that 'search' for large blobs of green matter, indicating fields, or large rectangular-shaped objects, indicating houses. If fields are located, then the computer goes on to search for items such as cows, horses, hedgerows and so on.

If the robot sees houses, it realises that it is in a built-up area and looks for roads and people. This is far more sensible than searching for, say, battleships or combine harvesters – objects that it may

125

know something about but which would be out of place in its current surroundings.

The knowledge about expected scenes would be built into packages stored in the machine's memory called *schemas*. Thus the robot would have a schema for fields, which contains knowledge about trees, cows and so on. It would have another schema for town settings, and countless others, for instance about the seaside, the insides of houses and what happens inside cafés. With enough schemas, the robot would feel reasonably familiar anywhere. The machine would certainly never embarrass someone accompanying it, by staring or pointing at things it doesn't recognise. Instead it would quietly get on with the job of understanding what they are – just like a well-behaved human. The concept of 'schemas' would also help robots to find their way around.

Consider, for instance, a robot that travels on wheels and which picks up information through TV cameras. Once it realises it is in a street, it activates its 'street schema' that contains information about lamp-posts, grass verges and cars. When it sees a doorway which it would like to enter, the robot moves towards it; once inside, it requires a new framework of knowledge, the room schema. The machine might then perceive a rectangular form, which, in the context of the room schema, suggests a window. The device then checks this situation. It works out if the rectangular form touches the floor. As it does not, the hypothesis is correct, at which point a 'window schema' is activated, and the robot looks for curtains or images of the outside world perceived through the glass.

With this schema process, the robot makes layer upon layer of deductions about its surroundings and activates its arms or other effector organs where appropriate. For instance, once inside the room, if it perceives that the window's curtains are closed, it would reach out to open them. If, in a factory, a robot perceived that, say, a machine tool is defective, it would find the faulty items and replace them.

A rather less ambitious robot than one with a complete library of schemas for different situations could be in routine operation inside factories by the end of the 1980s. This is a robot-on-wheels being developed by a team led by Mike Larcombe at the University of

Warwick near Coventry. The device will look like an industrial cart of the kind that trundles around in warehouses and on factory floors. The unusual thing about it is that it is driverless.

Instead of a driver, the contraption has a computer mounted in the rear. This receives information from an array of sensors on the vehicle – a TV camera, infra-red scanner and sonic pressure probes – that indicate the position of the cart. An important part of the truck is a 'map' of its surroundings contained in the computer's electronic memory. The map is fairly simple: it contains information only about a specific place where the vehicle is expected to operate, the inside of a factory for instance. The map would be far more complex if the machine was intended to trundle around in a less structured environment – the open air for instance – or if it had to move in different buildings, when a number of 'schemas' would be required. Ivor Guild, a member of the Warwick team, says that it is better to concentrate on such relatively straightforward machines to prove the technology. The more complex robots that can move anywhere can come later.

The Warwick researchers think the robot could do a lot of the fetch-and-carry jobs common in factories. It could pick up things from stores and load them for example, into machine tools. Ultimately, versions of the contraption could act as mobile floor sweepers, or mechanical nightwatchmen that look out for fires or intruders. Lansing Bagnall, a leading fork-lift truck manufacturer, is helping to support the research. It may use the results in advanced versions of its existing products.

It will be some time before we see in our everyday lives robots with the perception of a human. But already, one of the first A.I. robots is going through its paces. This is at the United States Navy's Naval Air Rework Facility in San Diego, California, where an experimental A.I. machine is taking out rivets from damaged aircraft. Normally this job is done by people; but the task is monotonous and sometimes dangerous: bits of metal from extracted rivets can fly out and strike workmen in the face. The robot has a TV camera which looks for rivets; and, importantly, the computer which analyses the TV pictures does so with rudimentary A.I. so it 'learns' the pattern of the rivets it has just taken out. Then the machine guides the stepping motors that move it over the plane's surface to the next place where, according to this pattern, it expects a rivet to be. Instead of casting around aimlessly for rivets with its TV 'eye' the robot has a good chance of predicting their exact positions.

The humanoid robot

Many of today's robots, we have seen already, are reasonably good at movement. They take things out of bins and load them onto conveyor belts, or they spray paint onto the panels of cars. People therefore feel the devices are pretty clever; we start to look at them with something approaching awe.

This response is, however, clearly inappropriate when we consider that today's robots are totally incapable of actions that a three-year-old child does without thinking – walking, holding a knife and fork or sitting in a chair for instance. How can engineers devise machines that move like people?

A big stumbling block, as in many other areas of artificial intelligence research, is that we don't know very much about *how* people do even the most simple actions. No one thinks about it when they, say, pick up a pen to write a letter. The movement is unconscious with no discernible effort in controlling the individual stages in the action. Once again, robot researchers have to turn to other disciplines – psychology and physiology – to find out how to devise plans that can be stored in a computer for generating action sequences.

In a similar way as in the problem of perception, A.I. researchers who want to make robots move like people turn to a 'layered' approach. They develop models of actions in which different levels of control influence what is done. When typing words with my typewriter, at one level my brain perceives the keys of the machine; another part of the brain decides what words are needed to convey the meaning of a thought pattern; and, on a further level, another control process commands my fingers to strike the keys to transfer the words to paper. The different levels of translating thought into action probably start at an abstract stage, in which details are not important and then, at the lower levels of the control process, describe the intricacies of the movement that is required. We can imagine that in a simple action such as the movement of a finger to press a button, one control 'layer' gets the arm broadly into the correct position; another moves the hand; and a further layer pushes the fingers into the right position.

If engineers want to build robots that move like people, not only will they have to attend to control factors; they must also design the device's mechanical appendages to resemble more closely human limbs. The mechanical parts of today's robots are a reasonable approximation to the arms of people; but as substitutes for arms they fall a long way short.

Researchers at the Massachusetts Institute of Technology, among others, are trying to improve matters. The Massachusetts workers reason that the current generation of robots finds difficult delicate operations which humans can manage perfectly well because of the compliance in their limbs. When, for instance, you rub your hand up against a wall, two factors permit you to stroke the surface gently instead of bruising your hand. First, your sense of touch tells you when your hand makes contact with the wall. Secondly, the compliance in your arm lets it stop at the right moment, rather than continuing in the direction in which it is travelling – which would cause injury. The researchers are therefore building a robot arm in which pulleys and cords replicate the muscles and tendons of the human limb.

A computer controls these mechanisms according to the activity that it wants the arm to undertake. A humanoid arm of the type in the experiment could conceivably have a touch sensor which lets it locate solid surfaces. Signals from the sensor then pass to the computer which instructs the arm how to operate. Because of its construction, the mechanism could do delicate tasks; for example, it could follow the contours of a curved surface or reach out and touch a person's face without risking injury. Industry involves many tasks – assembly jobs for instance – where such sensitive robots would be useful. Also, they could have other applications, as substitute limbs for people who have had arms amputated, for instance.

The first robots with *legs* may not look like humans at all. They are likely to have not two but six or eight such lower limbs. Research has shown that robots with two legs have great difficulty walking.

They end up looking like John Cleese doing his 'Ministry of Silly Walks' sketch. Six or eight legs give the contraption better balance and the ability to walk over rough terrain. So, in the near future at least, we are likely to become acquainted not with anthropoid robots but with ones that resemble mechanical beetles.

The expert machine

Perhaps the most fast moving area of research in artificial intelligence concerns 'expert systems'. These are computers that contain hundreds, if not thousands, of rules similar to those with which people solve everyday problems. Consider such a problem: someone's car has gone wrong and he needs to repair it. Systematically, the driver looks for faults in a particular part of the car such as the engine; if this is misfiring, the budding mechanic searches for something that would cause the problem, for instance a faulty spark plug. The thought process continues along definite pathways, entrances to which are opened by observations about how the car is performing.

If you were to plot a diagram of this person's line of thought, it would resemble a 'tree' structure; the thought processes would start at the bottom of the 'trunk' and pass along successive tiers of 'branches' according to whether observations match sets of logical rules. These rules are of the form '*If* condition A is true and *if* condition B is false, then there is an X per cent probability that condition C is true'. For instance, one such rule could be: 'If the car is misfiring and the spark plugs are badly worn, then there is a seventy per cent probability that the electrical timing mechanism is faulty'. In almost every area of human activity, it is possible to think of rules such as this which – subconsciously or not – people put into effect when arriving at conclusions. If you don't believe me, try thinking about how you think. You will soon arrive at a few basic rules that your thought processes obey.

Workers in expert systems believe that virtually *all* the thought patterns of humans can be represented by sets of rules of the kind just described. To formulate these rules, a computer researcher normally has to interrogate an expert in the area under discussion

130

for hours on end to find out how this mind works – what are the rules that he obeys. The rules are fed into a computer, which, if it contains sophisticated enough software, can be consulted by other people.

So to devise a computer system that knows a great deal about car repairs, a researcher would have to question a first-rate mechanic to find out his reasoning processes. The knowledge, fed into a computer, would be available to anyone who wants it. In this way, the computerised expert system becomes a modern, science-based oracle of the kind that was popular in ancient Greece. People consult the system for the information it contains, which is based on the wisdom of someone who may be dead, or on the other side of the world.

Now you may find it hard to believe, stomach even, that all human thought can be translated into a bare set of rules, no matter how complex and with how many sophisticated branches and forking mechanisms to permit twists and turns in reasoning. 'What about inspiration?' you might ask. 'Did rules alone let Beethoven compose his symphonies or Keats his poems?' If you disagree with the artificial intelligence community in this matter, then it will be hard to win you over. Feelings about computers that think, as I have already said, go very deep.

But whether or not you believe in the theory behind them, useful expert systems already exist. Researchers at Stanford University in California have produced several such systems which diagnose diseases in humans. In these, a computer holds thousands of rules that have emanated from skilled physicians. Other, less brilliant doctors feed into the computer observations about their patients; the machine then 'reasons' from these observations what is likely to be wrong.

In another example, BP, the oil company, wants to use research in artificial intelligence done at the University of Edinburgh. When an oil platform malfunctions, the signs of a fault are probably glaringly obvious: oil starts gushing out of a pipe at the wrong place for instance. But identifying the fault may be extremely difficult. Probably only a few engineers in each oil company are sufficiently expert in the design of platforms to be able to work out what is wrong; and as the engineers could be thousands of kilometres away, it could be expensive to bring them to the scene of every accident.

So BP wants to devise a system that is expert in the mechanism of oil platforms which contains all the knowledge of a highly skilled engineer. Less gifted technicians could consult this when 'blow-outs' or similar events occur to pinpoint their cause.

In a similar venture, Schlumberger, a firm that specialises in prospecting for oil, is experimenting with an expert system called Prospector. This contains the wisdom of experts in deciphering geological data to give the likely places for mineral deposits. The system could make it much quicker to find out from standard seismic surveys the probable sites of oil deposits.

Expert systems could be useful in manufacturing industry. As adjuncts to the groups of computerised, robot-operated manufacturing cells which will appear in the factories of the future, they could contain the knowledge of, for instance, engineers who are good at work scheduling. People would no longer need to inspect the data produced by a manufacturing cell – on, for instance, how well tools in the cells are performing – in order to give instructions for their use. Instead, the expert system would receive the information, consider it and then send out instructions accordingly.

One application of expert systems to manufacturing is already established. This concerns the production of mini-computers by DEC, a big American computer company. Mini-computers for different customers normally vary in detail. They contain the same basic components – standard boards of logic, memory modules and so on – but the number and arrangement of these parts depend on the specific use the customer wants for his machine. Translating a purchaser's requirement into a configuration for these components – there could be several hundred of them – represents a major headache for a computer company's sales force. To do the job well normally requires years of training. So DEC hit on the idea of feeding the wisdom of an experienced engineer into a computer; other people can interrogate it and apply the answers to production problems. Artificial intelligence researchers at Pittsburgh's Carnegie-Mellon University produced a system for DEC; and staff at some of its American manufacturing plants started to use it in 1980.

The conversational computer

Another subsection of artificial intelligence concerns ways of making machines understand ordinary human speech, either in the form of spoken words or of English sentences typed on paper. Normally, the only way that a computer understands anything from a human is for the latter to translate his thoughts into a special computer language which, in effect, puts ordinary words in the form of the binary computer code. Only people skilled in these languages can therefore get access to computers. It would be a lot easier if people could simply talk to these machines, or write them messages.

To train a machine to understand the human voice, it first must be fed sounds through a loudspeaker that it breaks down into the fundamental building blocks of the spoken language, called phonemes. Every word that you speak can be turned into perhaps a dozen or so of these phonemes. Then by analysing sequences of these building blocks – with sets of rules similar in concept to the ones used in other areas of A.I. – the machine rebuilds them into patterns that it recognises. Workers at IBM's research centre at Yorktown Heights, New York, have trained a machine to 'understand' simple phrases; here the machine successfully prints out the words spoken to it by a person.

The next step is to train robots to do things according to spoken commands. General Electric in the US is researching into 'listening' robots that their masters command by speaking. In Britain, Ferranti is working on a speech recognition equipment that could be useful in aeroplanes; with this pilots could simply tell their aircraft to steer in a certain direction instead of pressing buttons or pulling levers.

In other research centres, activity is rather more advanced in making machines that can talk back. It is technically not too difficult to translate the streams of binary digits from a computer's brain into signals that activate a loudspeaker and result in human-type sounds. True, the sounds are rather Dalek-like at present. But the 'Speak and Spell' educational aid that Texas Instruments developed in the late 1970s shows what can be done. The gadget 'speaks' simple phrases in accordance with buttons pushed by the user. The words don't sound like those of a human ... but who would want a computer, or a robot, to speak like a person? Nothing would scare people more.

In making computers understand written text, advanced work has been done at Yale University. A Yale program called FRUMP can extract précis of newspaper stories which it receives over a tele-printer line. It can condense a long story of, say, twenty paragraphs into a terse statement of a few sentences. Another system called CYRUS contains a lot of information about the former US government official Cyrus Vance – the Yale researchers chose him merely because he was a person in the news – and can answer questions about his life; the computer makes deductions, draws inferences and uses 'intuition' to piece together conclusions about the man even though it has not been directly told them.

Yet another system called BORIS is told stories and then answers questions about them. Here the computer can understand some of the nuances and illogicalities with which people talk and write. For instance, it has to know the difference between sentences such as 'Jack is in bed with a cold' and 'Jack is in bed with Doris'. It also has to understand that when someone says, 'Bill went to a bar and ordered a drink' Bill placed his order with a barman or similar person and not with a drinking companion. In other words, it has common sense. The machine gets this by being fed with a lot of information in the shape of 'expectation schemas' similar to those which A.I. researchers working on perception supply to their devices.

The future with artificial intelligence

A.I. systems require very large memories for storing knowledge and tremendously quick processing chips to analyse data in minute fractions of a second. Without these elements, provided at a reason-able price, artificial intelligence would never leave the drawing board. The great advances in computer technology during the 1970s have, therefore, helped A.I. researchers enormously. Today's computers fit into the space of small sideboards, process data in a matter of billionths of a second and have enough storage space to contain all the information in the books of the British Library, with

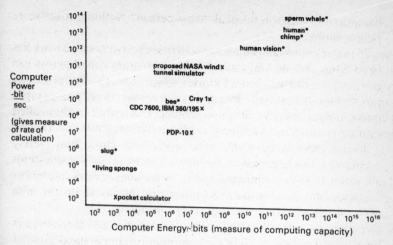

Fig. 8: Computer power and energy of various devices.
Scales are logarithmic.
Source: Hans Moravec, Carnegie-Mellon unit.

room to spare. Due to the cost reducing effects of microelectronics, such computers cost only a few tens of thousands of pounds, well within the budgets of many research institutes.

Figure 8 represents the computer power that is available now, compared with the 'brain power' of humans and other natural phenomena. While a little speculative, the diagram, which was devised by computer researcher Hans Moravec of Carnegie-Mellon University, gives some idea of how close the very fastest and powerful computers are to the raw 'intelligence' power of animals.

Where will we see the first applications of A.I. and advanced robotics? Probably not in manufacturing industry. Rather, the initial breakthroughs will come in easy-to-use computers – electronics firms are already working hard on these – and in areas where the governments of developed countries traditionally like to spend a lot of money. Yes, you've guessed it, these concern military applications.

The US Navy already has several projects which involve A.I. The Navy is developing 'intelligent' underwater vehicles that can understand where they are going. In one project, at the Naval Oceans

Systems Centre in San Diego, engineers are building a torpedo-shaped underwater craft that will steer out to underwater pipelines to pinpoint defects and take pictures. The craft, which will be virtually autonomous of controllers on land, should save oil and gas companies the time and effort of sending out divers to inspect underwater installations. But the development could have its more ominous applications. The underwater craft would be very good at laying mines or at disabling enemy ships or submarines.

The US Navy is sponsoring other work at Carnegie-Mellon University in which researchers are building an intelligent machine on wheels. The vehicle, guided by a TV camera, could be fitted with a robot arm for picking things up. Later, this machine and the one under development in San Diego could be 'married', perhaps to give some kind of amphibious craft. Hans Moravec is the principal researcher involved here: he also worked on a similar moving robot called The Cart, which was built at Stanford University.

Robots could also be used in the battlefields of the future. Delegates at an automation conference in Washington DC in November 1980 were given a talk about 'battlefield robots of the 21st century' which included a discussion of robots 'with command and control functions, surveillance functions, logistics functions and killing functions'. It is only too easy and alarming, to visualise how ultra-sophisticated walking robots could provide government with willing, expendable and totally ruthless armies. In the USSR, the Leningrad Institute of Aviation Instrumentation has published research into walking machines with six or eight legs. Their purpose can only be guessed at; but presumably they are for marching long distances over rough terrain – into neighbouring countries perhaps?

Mobile robots could have other, purely peaceful, uses – moving around the home or sweeping up litter in streets. But perhaps the most promising application is not on Earth at all, but in outer space. If we are ever to travel very far in the Solar System – and indeed outside it – robots will be used to help prepare the way. Even more important, robots could play a crucial role in what will be a feature of industrial life next century – the space factory.

Chapter Thirteen
Factories in space

'Continued growth of our human-created industrialised world can only occur if we move off Earth and permanently into space.' So says David Criswell of the California Space Institute in San Diego. Criswell is one of the leaders of a small group of Americans who, for several years, have been urging the rest of us to take seriously the idea of building and making things in space. If events turn out as they predict – and, given the amazing changes that the world has seen over the past fifty years, who is to dismiss these ideas out of hand? – then the world is in for a fifth industrial revolution some time next century. The revolution will usher in the era of the space factory.

Why would anyone want to build factories in space? There are two main reasons. First, under conditions of weightlessness and near vacuum, people may be able to make products which are difficult, or simply impossible, to fabricate on Earth. Secondly, space, if we define it as being anywhere outside the Earth's atmosphere, is far from empty. It contains, for a start, the Moon which we now know contains useful materials in abundance. At a time when people are worried about materials shortages on Earth, the Moon could be a godsend. If engineers are to mine the Moon for materials, it makes sense to construct factories there too. The products would either be transported back for consumption on Earth or, more likely, used to build things in outer space – satellites or large platforms for instance.

Already, elaborate plans exist in the scientific literature for space workshops on the Moon and even elsewhere in the Solar System. Mining the asteroids, the lumps of rock (some of them almost as big as the Moon) to be found in the outer reaches of the Solar System, is also a possibility, according to the enthusiasts. If we are to believe the estimates, people on Earth in the year 2010 will buy some £35 billion worth of goods made in space, by which time the industry would have generated two million new jobs in the US alone.

If these schemes seem outrageous, think about the Wright brothers and how people said that heavier-than-air flight was impossible. Now think of jumbo jets and the everyday acceptance of air travel. This example may not convince you about space manufacturing; but it will surely encourage you to keep an open mind.

If space factories do become part of industrial life, then robots and other kinds of automation will be sure to play a big part. For one thing, by the time such plants are constructed, the world will have advanced to a stage where no one would think of putting factories *anywhere* if they are not run by robots. Secondly, humans will never be very enthusiastic about working in the uncomfortable conditions of space – whether this be in orbit around the Earth or on the Moon. So manufacturers will simply be forced to use machines rather than people.

Space planners are interested in robots not simply because of their usefulness in future factories. NASA in the US, for instance, is investigating the machines for repairing satellites or other structures already in space. Technicians at the agency's Jet Propulsion Laboratory in California have made some progress in designing a wheeled robot that could move over the surface of a planet, perhaps Mars, seeing where it is going and picking up rocks. George von Tiesenhausen, the head of an automation team at NASA's Marshall Space Flight Center in Huntesville, Alamba, thinks that the agency will put a robot in space in about 1986, probably on board a space shuttle.

Not to be outdone, Western Europe is also interested in space robots. The French space agency plans to build such a machine and put it into orbit around 1990. It hopes to win support for the venture from other members of the European Space Agency which coordinates Western Europe's space projects. The French robot would repair satellites and do simple operations in orbiting space workshops similar to Spacelab, a big metal cylinder full of experiments that NASA's space shuttle will put into orbit in 1983. Machines such as those mentioned in the French proposals could virtually run a big space station called Solaris that the French are talking about putting into orbit in the 1990s.

Space robots will be the truly intelligent ones of the kind talked about in the previous chapter. In the inhospitable environment of space, humans will be better off if they keep right out of the way and let machines do all the work. It will also be far cheaper to put machines into space instead of people. To maintain a man in space for just one hour costs about £5,000, NASA has worked out, compared with the equivalent cost of £5–£50 per hour on Earth.

To ensure that the robots are true substitutes for people, they will have sensors such as artificial eyes. And they will interpret data and make decisions in much the same way as a human. That means giving the machines artificial intelligence; and it is no coincidence that, in recent years, a strong link has grown in the US between space specialists and workers from the A.I. community. A NASA study group on machine intelligence and robotics, which included many well-known names both from industry and academe, reported in 1980 that increased automation research 'will enhance significantly the cost-effectiveness and total information-return from future NASA activities'. Significantly, the study group also heavily criticised NASA for failing to keep up in the fast moving areas of artificial intelligence and related computer activities. Soon afterwards, NASA stepped up its total automation effort and now spends about £2.5 million on this annually.

Machines that do people's work for them in space are hardly new. Satellites and unmanned probes to other planets are simply tools which do jobs which humans would find either impossible or fiendishly difficult. But standard space hardware is normally controlled directly from Earth and cannot behave autonomously like a true 'intelligent' robot.

Even the two unmanned vehicles called Lunokhods that, as alternatives to manned missions, the USSR landed on the Moon in the early 1970s could not move independently. They were controlled by a five-man team at the USSR's space centre near Moscow. Looking at TV pictures that their vehicle supplied, the technicians had to steer it around obstacles such as boulders, always bearing in mind the delay of several seconds between the vehicle's movement and the reception of pictures on Earth. (The delay follows because radio waves travel at a finite speed, even though this is so large that on Earth, where the distances are so much shorter, we seldom realise it.) The effort was so immense that some of the navigators had to be hospitalised for mental and physical exhaustion. Of course the difficulties would be magnified still greater for similar 'teleoperated' vehicles that travel to points further away from Earth; the time delay for signals from Mars, for instance, is half an hour and that for Pluto about two days.

Such reasoning has convinced US researchers that, if they are serious about sending machines to explore the surfaces of far-away planets, the hardware must be able to act independently. Such vehicles would be able to move around to gather material and record data. The movement would not be random but would follow analysis, by the machine, of the sites that appear the most interesting.

But it is in space manufacturing that robots and other automated machines offer most – simply because this area appears to hold out the biggest rewards. The US is in danger of being left behind here by the USSR, which has launched several orbiting space stations for materials processing experiments. According to a report in 1980 from the US government's General Accounting Office, the Soviet Union has 350 top materials scientists researching into space manufacturing. The report was optimistic about the way space factories could help America. If the economics of space processing becomes favourable, 'the eventual national economic and social impact could be enormous'. In 1981, NASA was spending about £10 million annually on space manufacturing research, a long way short of what is really needed according to the enthusiasts.

Critics of the programme, who say NASA should move faster, include a group of scientists who meet every year at a conference at the University of Princeton to debate manufacturing in space. At the 1979 conference, David Criswell, Robert Ayres and Leslie Ayres produced a list of sixty-four types of goods, which, they claimed, could be made from materials from the Moon or with solar energy tapped in space. It would be boring to give the whole list but it includes products as diverse as guided missiles, engineering instruments, typewriters, earthenware food utensils, cutlery, clocks and watches, X-ray apparatus, ammunition, needles, pens, cooking equipment and children's games. 'Once a commitment is made to the use of extraterrestrial materials for manufacturing, the entire range of skills of an industrial society can be applied to enhancing the growth of the in-space enterprise,' the researchers stated. 'There is no single link . . . which could restrict the overall rate of growth of the combined materials and service segment of the economy.'

Let us examine in detail the grounds for this optimism. First, the Moon contains, in large quantities, a surprisingly large number of the elements with which industry on Earth constructs its products. The materials that the world consumes most voraciously are fossil fuels comprising hydrocarbons of various kinds; building materials such as silicon dioxide and calcium carbonate; metals, chiefly iron, aluminium, magnesium, copper zinc and lead; fertilisers for agriculture, mostly made from potassium, nitrogen and phosphorus; and other elements used in a variety of ways, for instance oxygen, sodium and chlorine. Virtually all these elements are to be found in Moon rock. By chemical processing, it would be possible to make from such rock a whole range of materials used in industrial products – structural materials, plastics, lubricants, adhesives, electrical materials and so on.

Providing engineers find some way of getting the materials out of the ground – and conventional mining techniques could do this – shortage of resources should not prove a problem for the operators of space factories. Now although building factories in space, either on the Moon or in orbit around the Earth, will bring obvious difficulties, some benefits accrue from making things away from the Earth. The chief of these is cheap energy. On Earth, we feel nothing of the real power of the Sun; much of the strength of its radiation is dissipated in the atmosphere before it reaches the ground. Although this arrangement is overwhelmingly to our advantage – without the atmosphere human life could not exist – it also means the Earth misses out on a lot of free energy. In space, however, the Sun's rays can be collected while they are still at their full power to produce, via solar cells, huge amounts of electricity.

Then again, conditions in space are very helpful for certain kinds of processing. For instance, in the near vacuum of space, crystals could be grown more easily than on Earth. Semiconductor materials could be grown and purified, as could glasses, for instance for ultra-pure fibre-optic cables, and metallic and gemstone crystals. Without oxygen, substances that are normally explosive could be handled with comparative ease; thus silanes, compounds of silicon and hydrogen which ignite on the Earth in the presence of oxygen, could be produced fairly easily. Silane production on the Moon could be very important as it may be possible to substitute silanes for traditional rocket fuels such as hydrogen or kerosone; with a silane plant, the Moon would have its own supply of propellant with which to power out-going spacecraft. New kinds of alloys could be prepared under gravity; separation of liquids through electrophoresis could take place more readily than on Earth; and workers (or robots) could handle highly sensitive materials, which on Earth react immediately with the receptacles in which they are held, rather more easily, using techniques of containerless processing.

A final advantage of making things on the Moon is that, if the products are required elsewhere in space, it is much cheaper to transport them there than from the equivalent factory on Earth. The Moon has no atmosphere; and its gravitational pull is much smaller than the Earth's. Therefore the cost of launching materials into orbit with a rocket could be as little as one thousandth of the equivalent cost from the Earth. The price of putting things into space has gone down remarkably – it now costs £1,500 per telephone circuit to put into orbit a communications satellite, a tenth of the figure a decade ago. But the cost reductions of the future will never make it possible for Earth rockets to compete on price with those that take off from the Moon.

Already, we put into space a surprising amount of material. Since 1959, the Earth has lost 5,000 tonnes of matter to outer space in this way; this works out at twenty kg per hour of propellant and ten kg per hour of space hardware. Much of this matter could conceivably have been processed in outer space using lunar materials.

In the future, however, we are sure to see far greater volumes of material used in orbiting space stations and large satellites – which increases the point of obtaining the matter from the Moon. A much

142

discussed project that would use something like 100,000 tonnes of material is a solar-power satellite; this would 'catch' sunlight in space, turn it into microwaves and beam it to receiving antennae on Earth. A network of such satellites – each a massive twenty km long and five km wide – could solve the world's energy problems. Virtually all of each craft could be made from silicon, aluminium, graphite, copper and iron – all of which could be produced from materials on the Moon.

Factories on the Moon are hardly likely to appear in the next couple of decades. To begin with, scientists want to increase their knowledge of what happens to materials in space with fairly unambitious experiments, for instance using the Spacelab launched by the space shuttle. If all goes to plan, the space shuttle will eventually prove itself as the first re-usable spacecraft, cutting enormously the cost of taking things into space. The idea of rockets that are almost completely destroyed while carrying a payload – this has been the fate of all pre-shuttle launchers – will then seem as absurd as the concept of throw-away airliners.

A modest space factory, almost completely unmanned, could follow soon afterwards. According to a report on future space projects prepared in 1980 by a team at the University of Santa Clara, it would comprise four parts: a furnace in which solar energy vaporises solid metal to produce powders of different materials; a separator which grades the resultant powders according to their size; a mixer to form the powders into a predetermined shape (this would use the principle of cold welding under which powders in a vacuum instantly coalesce); and a final cutting and assembling area. Figure 9 sets out how the plant would work.

At the same time as these experiments are taking place, structural engineers would learn more about how to build very large space platforms which could form the basis for fully fledged factories. These would be made with a large degree of automation: playing a big part would be versions of what is called the automated beam builder which Grumann of New York has built for NASA. This is a module that is fitted to a space shuttle and extrudes aluminium or plastic beams to make a lattice-like framework that could form the basis of large platforms. NASA's Johnson Space Center in Houston

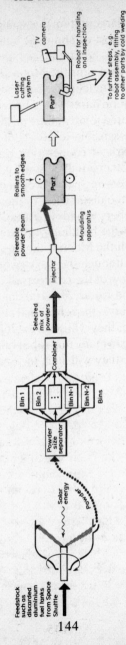

Fig. 9: Plan of Space Factory (Drawing from New Scientist, 23 April 1981)

has under study a very large station that could be built in space at the end of the 1980s at a cost of about £2 billion.

The next step would be to retrace the path of the Apollo astronauts and make tracks for the Moon. This time, however, the stay would be rather more lengthy than the ones enjoyed by these people. Permanent Moon bases would be set up perhaps – dare one hope for it – administered jointly under an international agreement. It would be far more sensible to go about the exploration of the Solar System in a spirit of cooperation rather than competition. First, bulldozers and other equipment would start mining. Then the first factories and processing works would be installed. In essence, they would work not too dissimilarly to those on Earth; beams and other structural members would weigh far less, however, and this would be reflected in the buildings' architecture.

The first workers on the Moon will be people. Not that they will enjoy it that much. Although the wages would be high, working in space suits and with few of the comforts of ordinary life will not be much fun. Later – and we are now talking about the first twenty years of the next century – the robots will move in. If some people's predictions come true, they will soon exhibit that most animal-like of tendencies, proving to many that robots are at last becoming truly anthropomorphic . . . they will start to reproduce.

Chapter Fourteen
The robot breeder

The science of self-reproducing automata had its beginnings in a lecture hall at the University of Illinois in December 1949. There John von Neumann, one of the most gifted thinkers of the 20th century, delivered a series of five talks under the general title 'the theory and organisation of complicated automata'. The Hungarian-American mathematician, who had already given the world several valuable guidelines (which are still adhered to today) on how to build and use computers, was bent on constructing a general theory of machinery. In particular, he was entranced by the possibility that advanced machines could resemble biological systems in their ability to reproduce.

In 1952, von Neumann started writing a book, provisionally called *The Theory of Automota Construction, Reproduction, Homogeneity*. He seemed to lose interest after a year or so and, when he died in 1957, the book was still unfinished. A colleague, Arthur Burks, edited the manuscript and added to it other material from von Neumann's lectures. Ultimately the work was published in 1966 under the title *Theory of Self Producing Automota*.

Disciples of von Neumann's work have developed his theories further and are out to grab any chance of seeing the ideas put into practice; and what better place in which to do this than on the Moon? For all his brilliance and foresight, von Neumann himself would hardly have guessed that, so soon after his death, people would be seriously talking about using his theory in the early stages of mankind's journey into the Solar System.

The ideas were discussed at a summer study run by NASA at the University of Santa Clara in 1980. The study, it should be said at once, was meant to stimulate ideas and was not too concerned whether they could be put into practice in the near future. Thus it talked in general about space factories, artificial intelligence and

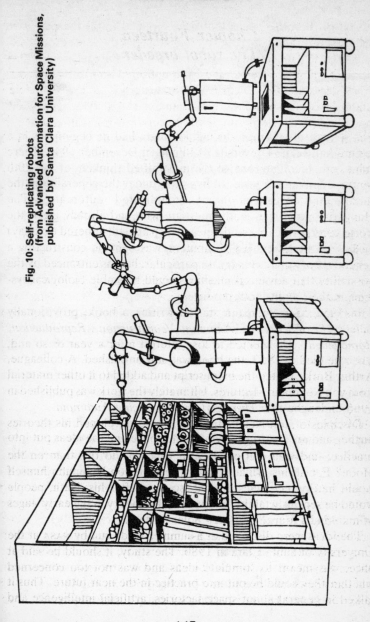

Fig. 10: Self-replicating robots (from Advanced Automation for Space Missions, published by Santa Clara University)

several of the other ideas that have cropped up in the past two chapters. With a fair degree of understatement, the study group said in its report, 'The design and construction of a fully self-replicating factory system is a tremendously complicated and difficult task.' Nonetheless the team, which was drawn from several academic establishments as well as NASA, recommended that the space agency should start to develop a simple laboratory-scale replication system. One of the first steps, it was thought, would be to take a simple robot to bits and program another one to put it together again. Later, robots could be trained to make other robots from a series of parts presented to them (Figure 10). The team said that its concept could have important consequences: 'It will accelerate the development of sophisticated automated assembly techniques useful in carrying out NASA missions, and of improved automated assembly and processing techniques applicable to the problems of achieving increased Earth-based manufacturing productivity.'

Furthermore, a robot-run factory on the Moon which would turn out not only products, but build new factories as direct replicas, would increase astoundingly mankind's ability to tap the resources of the Moon at a relatively low cost. Looking even further into the future, the Santa Clara researchers said their lunar manufacturing facility 'could be a stepping stone to the design and construction of replicating manufacturing complexes on the surfaces of other planets. These new complexes might themselves be the offspring of automated self-replicating factories'.

How would such a factory work? The theory was laid down by von Neumann. He postulated that a self-reproducing automation must have four components. Component A is an automatic factory which collects raw materials and turns them into products according to a written instruction. Component B is a duplicator, which takes a written instruction and copies it. Component C is a controller, linked to both A and B. When C is given an instruction, it first passes the instruction to B for duplication, then to A for action, and finally supplies the copied instruction to the parts that A produces. Component D is a written instruction which contains the specification that lets A manufacture anew a complete system, A plus B plus C. The most amazing part of von Neumann's theory was that, by

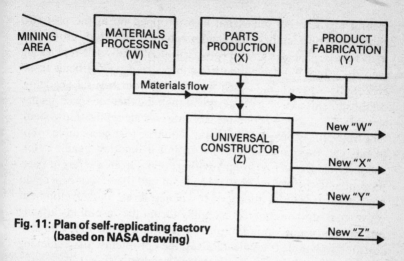

Fig. 11: Plan of self-replicating factory (based on NASA drawing)

talking about machines, he correctly postulated the way that human cells reproduce. A few years after his 1949 lectures, the biologists Crick and Watson discovered the structure of DNA, which led to the confirmation that nature's system is roughly as the mathematician had described.

An engineering blueprint for a factory built according to von Neumann's theory was produced in July 1980 by Georg von Tiesenhausen and Wesley Darbro of NASA. A plan would look something like Figure 11. The facility would have four main components. The first three are a processing unit, which would mine materials from the surrounding area and refine them; a production system which makes sub-assemblies and parts from materials fed to it from the processing unit; and a production facility, which turns out complete products. These components are all stocked with robots, machine tools, testing equipment and so on. Finally, we have what is called the universal constructor. The latter is the key to the whole system. It takes parts from the production system and, with them, turns out complete new factories. As these, of course, contain their own universal constructors, the process begins all over again, so that factories self-replicate at an exponential rate (Figure 12).

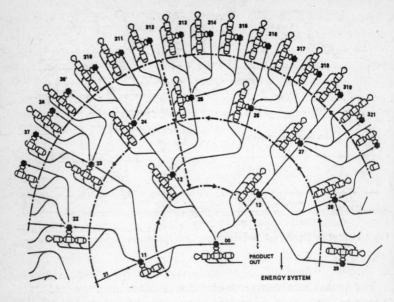

Fig. 12. Growth plan of Moon factory (NASA drawing).

Each universal constructor would itself comprise two parts – a stationary unit and several mobile robots. Parts are transported to the stationary unit by conveyor from a warehouse. On the stationary unit, the mobile machines go to work on the parts, moving them off if necessary to a construction site. The whole process would be supervised by a master controller somewhere in the middle of the universal constructor (Figure 13).

According to the Santa Clara study team, as well as self-replicating, the lunar factory could make a huge range of useful products. These would include components for space vehicles, radio telescopes, and solar power satellites; and microelectronic devices, rocket fuels, machine tools, robots and solar cells. All these could be used by those hardy pioneers who had stayed on the Moon to look after the factories (for by now there would be more than one), or, more likely, the products would be boosted into space to serve either in orbiting stations or to be transported back to the folks back home on Earth.

150

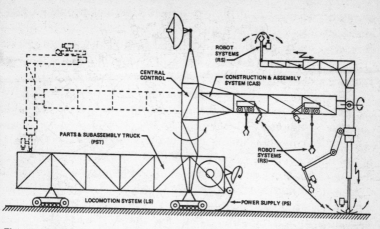

Fig. 13: Mobile Universal Construction Unit for Moon factory (NASA drawing).

The Santa Clara team envisaged that its initial factory would take a year to produce an offspring. At this rate, after ten years, there would be about 1,000 of the plants. This is where the growth really starts to take off: a million after twenty years and 1,000 million after thirty years. Either humans will have to be pretty smart at stopping the factories when they are in full swing or they will rapidly have to make more space available for the plants. Presumably the computers which control the factories will contain inbuilt constraining mechanisms that stop them gobbling up raw material indiscriminately; otherwise at some stage the factory equipment could commandeer rockets which it has itself built, land on Earth and start making new materials out of people's houses. This is just one of a number of nasty things that could happen; I am sure you can imagine more. No wonder then, that the Santa Clara researchers, presumably to excuse themselves from thinking too deeply about the possible consequences of their ideas, proposed to NASA that it should not only examine the technical merit of their ideas but should 'initiate studies of the social, political and economic consequences of the proposed work'.

Why will the Moon workshops be necessary? Richard Laing, a

researcher at the University of Oregon, says that people's basic incompetence, rather than their technical brilliance, will force people to build factories in space and run them with advanced machinery. 'I would like to see the Earth living within its means. But I can see us messing things up even more if we remain on Earth – we will overpopulate, pollute and desecrate. So we may be forced to use extraterrestrial materials and to go elsewhere if we want to continue living on a high technical level.'

The vision of robots toiling away in the Moon factories that they have built themselves would no doubt have pleased Karel Capek, the man who, in literature at least, brought robots into the world. One day, the words that Capek gave to one of his characters (who, naturally is a robot) could turn out to be correct. 'The power of man has fallen. A new world has risen. The rule of the Robot.'

PART 5

Lessons

Chapter Fifteen
The Japanese experience

'To understand the Japanese approach to industry, you have to know a little about their culture. Take their martial arts for instance. They don't go out to disarm an opponent – they try to kill him.'

A British electronics engineer made this remark during a discussion about Japan's computer industry. As in several key areas, the Japanese have earmarked computers as a business in which they want world dominance. They are already well on the way in industries such as cars, robots, computer-controlled machine tools and electronic goods like TVs and video recorders. This striving for supremacy, according to those who say they understand the country, comes not because of any aggressive intent. Rather, Japan feels it has a mission in life – to show the world the best way into the next century.

Many people are discussing the prospects of the developed world turning into an 'information society' in which very few people work in factories. These are highly automated and virtually run by robots. The bulk of the population works in so-called 'knowledge industries'. They teach, think up new products, do research and development, devise computer software and work in a range of service jobs in which brains are more important than brawn. Japan, however, is the only place where the government has welcomed this trend wholeheartedly, and, what is more, is preparing to hasten it.

The Japanese government has invented a clumsy-sounding English word – mechantronics – for the new technological discipline which it says will be important in the next few decades. It means the merger of electronic control technology with straightforward mechanical products. The discipline produces two general types of material goods. The first is the computer-controlled machinery which will rapidly take over the factories. The second constitutes the new electronic products which, so the Japanese say, the peoples

155

of the world will need in their forthcoming information societies. Such products include a vast range of computerised gadgets for handling information in the most efficient way – word processors, language translators, computerised telephone exchanges and satellite links and equipment for calling up information from data bases.

'Mechantronics' is behind the startling Japanese love affair with the computer. From virtually nowhere in 1970, Japan has become, after the US, the world's second most powerful computer manufacturer. The country is content not just with building and using the machines; it also wants to dominate the design and manufacture of the integrated circuits that go into computers.

Japan's powerful Ministry of International Trade and Industry (MITI) spent some £100 million in the late 1970s either aiding or restructuring the country's electronics industry. The country has made amazing progress in making chips. In 1971 it made about 150 million integrated circuits; in 1979, the figure was ten times this. 'Chips will be used in embedded computers in a wide range of goods – cars, machine tools, wrist watches, and consumer goods,' one MITI official told me. 'We reject the view that we can buy the chips from abroad. We must create the technology from the beginning in order to reap the benefits of using it.'

MITI's views on how to prepare for the future have a schizophrenic tone. For the Japanese have a desperate inferiority complex. Japan is a small, not particularly beautiful country with so few natural resources that it must import fifty-five per cent of its food and ninety per cent of its energy. Leaving aside the Second World War, it is only in the past ten years that Japan's voice has counted for anything on the world's stage. The country feels that Europe and the US, which between them, have virtually done what they wanted with the world for the past dozen centuries, are culturally superior. It thinks, possibly quite wrongly, that it has much to learn from these places.

Furthermore, the country is almost ashamed that its success in world markets has resulted from imitating technologies developed in the West. So far, the Japanese have done virtually nothing new in technology. They started their own incredibly successful robot and computer businesses by first buying these machines from the West and copying how they work.

It is time, the Japanese have declared, to cast off the mantle of imitators and become innovators. Hence the idea of leading the world into a new kind of society. Japan is now trying desperately hard to get on with other nations so that the message can be spread around. The country is also stepping up its aid to developing nations. In the interests of world harmony, it feels that such countries should be helped to become self-sufficient in industrial technologies that are now in widespread use in the West. This will leave the way clear for Japan to shift its emphasis to the new so-called 'knowledge industries'.

The government attempts to achieve its plans in a way unfamiliar in the West. Civil servants are far closer to people in industry than their Western counterparts. While in Britain it is unusual for a government official to get a job in industry, or vice versa, this is common in Japan. MITI officials also have a close relationship with banks. Through informal meetings which sometimes last well into the night (more often than not in bars), banking and government officials reach a consensus as to which industries should be supported with cash, and what their broad policies should be.

Japan's government is no stranger to scheming about the future. It masterminded what it calls the *shotoku baizo*, or the 'income doubling period' in the twenty years after the Second World War. In this era, Japan built up its steel and heavy goods industries and embarked on a huge programme of modernisation. From a predominantly agricultural country in the early 1950s, the country's industrial workforce shot up from twenty-four per cent of the working population in 1955 to thirty-five per cent in 1970. In the 1970s, the economy expanded at a slower rate. But during this decade annual growth still averaged 5.4 per cent as compared to 3.2 per cent in West Germany, 2.9 per cent in the US and 2.2 per cent in the UK.

As part of this growth, Japan has concentrated on equipping its factories with modern machinery. Between 1953 and 1971, Japan's manufacturers invested twenty-three per cent of their sales in new plant and equipment. Italy reinvested nineteen per cent of its manufacturing revenue, Sweden sixteen per cent, France fourteen per cent and Britain just thirteen per cent.

In a survey of engineering industries in Japan in 1974–75, £4,500 was invested for every employee. In the UK, the equivalent figure was £400, according to the Department of Industry's automated small-batch production committee. In 1977, sixty-one per cent of British machine tools were over ten years old; in Japan the figure was forty per cent. And the Japanese are continuing to race ahead. Japan is increasing its machine tool capacity by something like three per cent per year, while the number of machines in Britain is declining.

At least part of the reason why Japanese industries invest more in equipment is that they get loan finance fairly cheaply. Often, they operate up to their ears in debt in order to buy the most modern hardware; and, by contrast with the UK, they take a long-term view regarding the equipment's usefulness. In the UK, many accountant-dominated companies insist that new machinery repay its cost in improved output within as little as one or two years. The demands are so stiff that the machinery is never bought.

The Japanese government's policy for the new 'information society' has several broad planks. First, it intends to increase its budget for scientific and technical research – an area in which Japan spends surprisingly little. In the late 1970s Japan spent something like 1.7 per cent of its gross domestic product on research, compared with 2.2 per cent in the US and West Germany, 2.0 per cent in Britain, and 1.8 per cent in France. And the state foots the bill for far less R&D than the West. It pays for just twenty-seven per cent of Japan's total research budget; in Western countries the figure is usually around fifty per cent. Where Japan has excelled is in the application, not the discovery, of good ideas. In MITI's words, the country now wants to become not only a 'technological harvester' but a 'planter' as well.

To this end the country plans to spend £200 million on a new generation of computers that uses original ideas developed in Japan (see Chapter 11). The computers would use principles of artificial intelligence so that people can use them easily. The machines would become especially useful in areas such as teaching, office work, general research and so on – which are just the sectors that the government wants to encourage. MITI also plans big spending programmes in such unrelated areas as aerospace, ceramics and biochemistry.

As a further strand to its strategy, MITI is anxious to make research and scholarship, as much as possible, a part of everyday living. The government enthuses about 'technopolises' (another ghastly English word that the Japanese have invented) in which laboratories coexist with houses, shops and other trappings of urban life. One such technopolis is already taking shape on the outskirts of Tokyo. This is Tskuba City, a new town where most of the government laboratories are sited. The government is paying the huge expense of shifting its science centres from their previous sites around the country because it believes the concentration of technical expertise will lead to better research.

The government also wants to attract scientists and engineers from abroad. It has in mind the kind of 'brain drain' in which, in previous years, young researchers have left Europe for the US. 'To train richly creative people with an international perspective,' says MITI, 'we must create new professional posts for foreign scholars and establish research laboratories boasting the best equipment available anywhere.'

Schooling is also important. The Japanese take great pride in their education statistics. Ninety per cent of their young people go to senior high school, where they stay until their late teens, and thirty-five per cent attend university. You should not draw too many conclusions from these figures. Westerners sometimes point out that the standard of teaching is poor and leaves pupils able to recite facts and figures but with little ability for inspired thinking. But the government's aim, which is worthy enough, is to prepare young people for work with their brains rather than their bodies.

The Japan Information Processing Development Centre, a body funded by MITI and leading electronics companies, presses the message home with a strong streak of hyperbole. 'Japan's most precious assets are its highly educated, hard-working, high quality and abundant work force and human resources. These should be used to form information .... into new resources that are as good as food or energy.'

Will the policy work? Japan certainly looks in better shape than most to transfer people from the manufacturing sector of the economy to services. For one thing, the shift that is required is not too great. Japan's industrial workforce has shot up from a small base only in the past thirty years; in the early 1970s, it reached a peak of about thirty-seven per cent of all those in employment, and then started to decline. By contrast, the economies of most European countries are geared to sustaining a larger proportion of industrial workers, though, in nearly all countries, this proportion is steadily falling (see Figure 14).

The changing composition of Japan's labour force during the 1970s, gives a clue as to how the information society could become feasible. Between 1973 and 1979, workers were squeezed out of manufacturing industry at an astonishing rate, an average of 8.2 per cent per year. The trend was only slightly less marked than in Britain, where, over the same period, manufacturing industry shed workers at a rate of 8.4 per cent – a factor which contributed to the country's high unemployment rate of ten per cent (in 1981). In the same year, the comparable figure for Japan was just over two per cent. Where did Japan's displaced manufacturing workers get new jobs?

The answer is: in services. Over the six years, people in this area in Japan leapt up by fourteen per cent. This sector comprises work in government offices, retailing, distribution and other non-manufacturing activities. Almost four million new jobs were created, more than enough to counterbalance the employment lost in manufacturing. (The new service jobs also soaked up the people displaced from agriculture and fishing, an area which, as in most developed countries, offers fewer job opportunities year by year because of changing social and economic trends.)

In Britain, as Table 4 shows, service jobs also rose – by 6 per cent, but with a work force that expanded over the period by about one million, the mechanism did not provide enough employment to compensate for the jobs lost in manufacturing (plus the 100,000 or so that disappeared in the construction industry).

Japan's shrinking force of manufacturing workers is the result of automation. More robots and machine tools equal fewer people. Automation has had a major effect: Japanese factories have

160

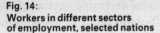

Fig. 14:
Workers in different sectors of employment, selected nations

'Agricultural' employment as % of all employment

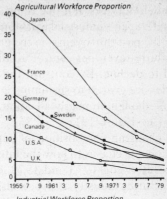

Production Industry employment as % of all employment

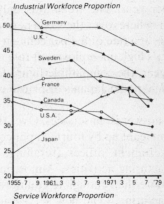

Service employment as % of all employment

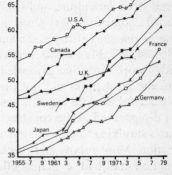

Source:
Science Policy
Research Unit,
(University of Sussex) and
Social Trends (UK Government)

NB: Production industry =
manufacturing + construction

increased their output prodigiously (Table 5). In 1973, 14.4 million factory workers produced $259 billion worth of goods. By 1979, eight per cent fewer people made goods worth over twenty per cent more. This translates into an overall productivity rise (measured in terms of output per person) of nearly thirty-two per cent.

In Britain's factories, by contrast, output per person in 1973 was a little more than half that in Japan. Over the next six years, matters got even worse. Productivity rose so slowly that by the end of the decade something like two-and-a-half British workers were required to produce the same value of goods as a single Japanese. Overall production hardly changed over the six years, and, since 1979, a bad situation has become catastrophic. By mid-1981 sales of British manufactured goods had fallen by more than one-fifth. There were one-eighth fewer workers in the industry. Anyone looking for increased productivity would have been sorely disappointed. The figure (measured in terms of output per person) fell in two years by eleven per cent. By early 1982, in fact, productivity had picked up again and was higher than the 1979 figure. But this was mainly because manufacturing industry had shed even more workers: output was still disastrously low.

Table 4. Change in employment structure, Japan and Britain, 1973–79

	JAPAN			BRITAIN		
Numbers in employment (millions)	1973	1979	% change	1973	1979	% change
Primary industry (agriculture etc)	7.0	6.1	−14	0.6	0.6	0
Manufacturing	14.4	13.3	−8	7.7	7.1	−8
Construction	4.7	5.3	+12	2.2	2.1	−5
Services	26.2	29.8	+14	12.2	13.0	+6
Total in employment	52.3	54.5	+4	22.7	22.8	+0.4
% workforce unemployed	1.3	2.0	—	2.6	6.7	—

Source: OECD and national figures

162

In a nutshell, the two countries illustrate the difference between a post-industrial society and one that is suffering from de-industrialisation. In the former, factories operate with fewer workers and more machinery and create wealth. This is spread through the economy to support other people who work in new types of jobs, such as services. With de-industrialisation, manufacturing industry sells steadily fewer goods; the number of workers falls calamitously; and, as so little wealth is being generated, little employment is provided elsewhere. The result is lengthening dole queues.

Individual Japanese firms have done remarkably well with automation. In 1980, Toyota employed the same number of people as five years before; yet in that time it increased production by fifty per cent. Mitsubishi, another car company, produced seven times as much in 1980 as a decade previously – with a workforce only fifteen per cent higher. Matsushita employs some 63,000 people, the same as in 1970, when sales were one third their present level. Fujitsu doubled sales in five years with virtually no increase in employees.

With Japan's efforts to produce intelligent robots and advanced machine shops, productivity will probably increase still further. The big Japanese firms are revving up their engines for still more astonishing feats. Matsushita, for example, plans to double its R&D staff over the next five years to 12,000; and in ten years, increase its robot population a hundredfold to 100,000.

Table 5. Manufacturing performance, Japan and Britain, 1973–79

	JAPAN			BRITAIN		
	1973	1979	% change	1973	1979	% change
Output ($ billions, '78 prices)	259	314	+21	78	77	−1
Employment (millions)	14.4	13.3	−8	7.7	7.1	−8
Output per person ($ thousand, '78 prices)	18.0	23.6	+32	10.1	10.8	+8

Source: OECD and national figures

Employees at the biggest Japanese firms have no need to fea
technology will make them redundant. The giants operate the fam
ous principle of 'lifetime employment'; if a technical innovation
displaces a person from his job, he is found another one elsewhere
But this principle is less widely applied than is usually thought
According to some observers, only about ten per cent of the work
ing population is covered by such agreements. The others are in
much the same position as people in the West; if automation i
introduced and demand for products does not rise in accordance
with the extra productivity made possible, they will probably be ou
of a job. Hence the onus in Japan on expanding output.

Japan has been increasing production from its factories at an
astonishing rate. There are two components to the increased sales
First, Japan itself is still a fast growing economy with a big demand
for manufactured products. The average Japanese spends half a
much again as a UK person on goods and services. But, more
significantly, the Japanese channel much more of their disposable
income into investment – which in turn leads to demand for manu
factured goods from new factories, offices and other big projects. In
1977, for every 100 yen that a Japanese household had free fo
spending twenty-one yen was saved. The equivalent percentage fo
the UK is ten; for West Germany, twelve; France thirteen; and the
US, five. In the economy as a whole, fixed investment as a propor
tion of total spending is far higher than in other developed countrie
(Table 6). High demand at home for goods is more likely to benefi
domestic industries than in other countries because the proportion
of manufactured goods in total imports is relatively low. This i
about twenty-three per cent, compared to some thirty per cent in
Britain.

The second reason that Japan's factories are working ever more
furiously (though they may contain fewer workers) is the country'
astonishing export performance. The country's share of total manu
factured exports produced by the industrialised countries shot up
from 5.1 per cent in 1955 to 15.6 per cent in 1978 (Table 7). In tha
year, Japan overtook the US as an exporter of manufactured goods
Although people often think otherwise, Japan doesn't put an over
whelming proportion of its resources into the export drive. It sell

Table 6. Fixed investment as proportion of GNP

	UK	France	West Germany	Italy	US	Japan
Average 1950–54	14	18	20	19	17.5	21.5
Average 1970–75	19	24	24	21	17.5	33.5

Source: The Economics of Technological Progress, edited by Tönu Puu and Sören Wibe, Macmillan

overseas only about ten per cent of all its goods and services; the equivalent figure for Britain is around twenty-three per cent. Rather, exports (particularly in recent years) have been racing ahead of other sectors of the economy. In the year to March 1981, for instance, only a quarter of the overall growth in the economy of five per cent was due to home consumption. The rest was attributable to increased exports, which grew by a fifth.

The nature of the goods sold to foreigners has been changing, too, reflecting the trend toward 'mechantronic' goods. General machinery, which in 1965, accounted for twenty per cent of the country's goods sold overseas, registered thirty-six per cent in 1978. The other big developer was the car business, whose share leapt from three per cent to sixteen per cent. By contrast, the share of heavy industries, which Japan's rulers are suggesting are no longer profitable, declined. The proportion in total exports of textiles, steel and ships

Table 7. Shares of industrialised countries in manufactured exports

	1955	1965	1975	1977	1978
UK	19.8	13.9	9.3	9.3	9.5
US	24.5	20.3	17.7	15.9	15.2
West Germany	15.5	19.1	20.3	20.8	20.7
France	9.3	8.8	10.2	9.9	9.8
Japan	5.1	9.4	13.6	15.4	15.6
Italy	3.4	6.7	7.5	7.4	7.9

Source: as Table 6

fell in 1978, to five, thirteen and six per cent compared with eighteen, fifteen and nine per cent in the mid 1960s.

Not surprisingly, the export growth, specially in areas such as cars and electronic goods, is souring relations overseas. Japan's trade surplus with the EEC for the first six months of 1981 soared by more than fifty per cent (compared with the same period a year before) to a record £2.8 billion. With long dole queues in much of the West, the cries are that Japan is 'exporting unemployment'. Many Europeans – and Americans – are talking about barring Japanese exports to give their own industries time to retool, reorganise and compete along Japanese lines. To forestall this kind of pressure, the Japanese government wants to increase overseas investment and, through joint ventures, provide jobs using Japanese technology on foreign soil. This spirit has led, for instance, to the joint British Leyland–Honda project to build cars in Oxford and the rash of Japanese electronics factories that are springing up in Britain. Japan's overseas investments totalled more than £2 billion annually in each of the three years from 1978.

Japan's growth is due not only to automated factories and clever imitation of technologies developed abroad. The flexibility, not to say docility, of the average Japanese worker plays a big part. In big companies, the workers belong to single trade unions that owe their allegiance to the firm rather than an amorphous outside body. This makes employees more willing to change jobs within the company and work with new machinery. Less time is bogged down in demarcation disputes and deciding who does what.

Further, employees simply work extremely hard. It is not uncommon to find Japanese car workers running from one part of a factory to another to get their jobs done more quickly. Surveys show that only twenty per cent of Japanese workers takes their full complement of holidays. They also go into work on Saturday mornings and in the evenings. Even if the machinery is shut down, they like to chat to their fellow employees, to decide on improved working methods for instance.

There are two ways of looking at this preoccupation with work. One is to say it is healthy: it has led to a booming economy and, indirectly, to increased material benefits for the Japanese population. Others say the 'workaholic' nature of many Japanese amounts to neurosis – a deep sickness in a society where people are so insecure that they cannot enjoy what leisure they have.

Attitudes are changing, however. English-speaking Japanese newspapers talk about a trend called 'my-homeism' which is threatening to establish itself. Sufferers of this affliction get the strange idea that they want to go home in the evenings instead of talking to their workmates in nearby bars about how to improve productivity. They begin to take their holidays and are concerned about finding decent places to live. (For all the country's affluence – gross domestic product per person is one and a half times that in Britain – Japanese houses and flats are generally cramped and dismal.)

The authorities are in two minds about this trend. In the long term, it can only be good. It encourages people to relax, think and develop the 'knowledge products' that the government is keen to promote. In the short term, however, the new thinking could damage the Japanese industrial machine and slow down the creation of wealth that the Japanese hope will support their 'information society'.

The dilemma is, however, not too serious. The Japanese have put their trust in automation . . . and the decision seems to be paying off. An efficient, wealth-creating manufacturing sector has, in effect, bought Japan time in which to think about what kind of society it wants to become. Britain, by contrast, has very little time . . . and what there is is running out.

Chapter Sixteen
What future for Britain?

For more than 100 years, Britain has been backing out of manufacturing industry. In Victorian times, gentlemen sent their sons to the Civil Service or to the City of London, and discouraged them from getting their hands dirty in factories. Governments paid lip service to technical education. After their sterling efforts in the first half of the 19th century engineers became second-class citizens. Much the same is true today. Many contemporary engineers lack the self-respect even to think of trying to raise their own status. These people's lack of social awareness does nothing to force the rest of society to recognise their true skills.

The disregard for the skills of the engineer and for the qualities needed in manufacturing, takes many forms. Scientists and engineers rarely attain the highest offices in the civil service and industry.

Newspapers put reports about the professional activities of 'respectable' people such as doctors and teachers in their main 'home news' pages. The doings of engineers, even though they may be of great importance to the future of the country, are shoved in at the back of the newspaper, in the business section. In London, the Royal Society of Arts, Manufactures and Commerce invariably shortens its name to the first four words. It sounds snappier, of course, but the abbreviation recognises that more people are interested in arts than in the dreary old business of manufacturing. (This way, presumably, the society gets a bigger membership.)

Further, Britain has a poor record in industrial research. Expressed as a proportion of gross domestic product, Britain's research spending is higher than most Western countries. But this is because so much cash goes on defence activities and other non-industrial areas such as nuclear power stations. The UK's industrial R&D spending per head of population was, in 1975, roughly half that

168

Table 8. Industrial R&D spending: international comparisons

	1967*	1972*	1975*	1975 Total ($m)	1975 Per head of population ($m)
US	109.7	102.5	100	23,540	110
West Germany	69.4	96.7†	100	5,874	95
France	85.2	97.5	100	3,645	69
Japan	52.6	103.7	100	5,637	51
UK	113.0	105.8	100	2,914	52

* 1975 = 100   † 1971 figure

Source: *Trade and Industry*, 6 April 1979

of West Germany and the US (Table 8). Even worse, while many other countries increased their spending in the decade before 1975, the UK's budget went down. The trend was arrested by 1978, but even within an enlarged total budget, the R&D cash spent on the key areas of mechanical and electrical engineering showed a worrying fall (Table 9).

The UK government shows a remarkable preoccupation with defence orientated research – at the expense of industrial R & D. The government is responsible for around half the country's total

Table 9. Industrial R&D spending, UK (1975 prices, £m)

YEAR	1967	1975	1978
TOTAL	1514	1340	1566
of which:			
Chemical	216	245	288
Mechanical	154	103	119
Electronics	285	279	442
Other electrical engineering	92	73	69
Motor vehicles	113	88	88
Aerospace	356	292	286
Other	272	213	228

Source: as Table 8 and *British Business*, 8 August 1980

research budget. According to a statement by Margaret Thatcher in the House of Commons in January, 1981, the state's R&D budget increased by a minimal six per cent between 1972 and 1981. Within this, defence spending increased by thirty-four per cent, while spending on industrial productivity and technology decreased by sixty-five per cent (Table 10). Out of every £1 that the British tax-payer spends on research, fifty-four pence goes on defence – on missiles, tanks, aircraft, communication equipment and so on. The comparable percentages for France and West Germany are thirty-three per cent and twelve per cent.

No one doubts that Britain must do military research. But is it so important that it should take up such a disproportionate share of the country's resources? Are Britain's military commitments really shooting ahead at a rate commensurate with the extra spending? Bearing in mind the importance of manufacturing to the UK, would it not be sensible to spend more on industrial R&D?

In recent years, three broad views have been proposed as to why Britain can afford to let manufacturing industry slowly wither away. The first body of opinion says that the oil wealth of the North Sea can replace the lost production in manufacturing industry. The second says that service enterprises will appear from the ruins of manufacturing industry and generate new jobs – we no longer need a strong secondary sector, according to this argument. The third

Table 10. British government spending on research and development 1972–1981 (£m at 1975 prices)

	1971–72	% of total	1980–81 (estimate)	% of total	% increase 1972–1981
Defence	561	43	755	54	+34
Energy	92	7	99	7	+7
Health	25	2	38	3	+52
Industry	231	18	80	6	−65
Planning	34	3	40	3	+17
Other	351	27	369	27	+5
Total	1,294	—	1,381	—	+6

Source: House of Commons answer, 22 January 1981

view says that we should not worry too much about reduced output and employment in manufacturing (and other areas as well). The trend reflects a long term switch to a society where fewer people have to work. Therefore, we should devise vast social service schemes to cope with an army of permanently unemployed people.

All three views are fallacies. They miss the point about manufacturing industry's relevance to Britain. The country simply cannot afford not to have an efficient manufacturing industry. What is more, the task of resurrecting it is not so huge as people might think.

Fallacy 1. The North Sea saviour

With North Sea oil, Britain no longer needs a strong manufacturing base. How true is this?

As a result of the oil, the UK no longer has to buy a lot of fuel from abroad. According to some people, if Britain wants to keep its trade balance roughly constant (this to ward off the nasty economic effects of changes in the overseas price of the pound) it has to reduce its exports. Therefore, manufacturing industry, which accounts for two-thirds of goods sold overseas, should decrease its output considerably. John Kay and Peter Forsyth of the Institute of Fiscal Studies have set out how they see the shape of the UK economy after North Sea oil has its effect (Table 11).

Kay and Forsyth see the UK economy growing by a total of five per cent in the years between 1976 (before the UK started bringing ashore much oil) and the mid 1980s. Production from the primary industries, which include oil, leaps from £9 billion to £19 billion. If other sectors of the economy – construction, services and public administration – grow at a reasonable rate, the only way that total output will keep within the five per cent increase is for manufacturing production to decrease by nine per cent. This assumes that expenditure on each of these items grows uniformly by about five per cent annually.

Kay and Forsyth do not try to predict the level of unemployment in the mid 1980s. But the burgeoning oil-generation industries can be expected to produce only few jobs. Growing at a relatively slow rate, services would not require many more people. With three

Table 11. Kay/Forsyth argument on how North Sea oil will change the structure of the UK economy

All figures in £ billion, 1980 prices; BO = 'before oil': 1976 economy; AO = 'after oil': mid 1980s economy; Balance = Production–Expenditure; Kay/Forsyth figures taken from the *Guardian*, 14 July 1980

Sectors of economy	Expenditure			Production			Balance	
	BO	AO	% change	BO	AO	% change	BO	AO
Primary industry (agriculture etc. plus oil)	15.8	16.7	+6	9.0	19.0	+111	−6.8	+2.3
Manufacturing	46.0	48.5	+5	48.9	44.7	−9	+2.9	−3.8
Construction	22.6	23.8	+5	22.5	24.3	+8	−0.1	−0.5
Services	86.2	90.9	+5	88.1	89.3	+1	+1.9	−1.6
Public administration	13.5	14.2	+5	13.5	14.6	+8	0	+0.4
TOTALS	184.1	194.1	+5	182.0	191.9	+5	−2.1	−2.2

Table 12. Alternative scheme for shape of economy in mid-1980s – with manufacturing-led growth

Sectors of economy	Expenditure			Production			Balance	
	BO	AO*	% change	BO	AO*	% change	BO	AO
Primary	15.8	17.5	+11	9.0	19.0	+111	-6.8	+1.5
Manufacturing	46.0	60.0	+30	48.9	60.1	+23	+2.9	+0.1
Construction	22.6	28.0	+23	22.5	27.0	+20	-0.1	-1.0
Services	86.2	108.3	+25	88.1	108.3	+22	+1.9	0
Public administration	13.5	14.6	+8	13.5	14.6	+8	0	0
TOTALS	184.1	228.4	+24	182.0	229.0	+23	-2.1	+0.6

* 'after-oil' economy based on following assumptions:

1) 1982 GDP of £207 billion

2) 5 years of 2% growth from 1982 to 1987, which gives total growth in economy from 1976–87 of 23 per cent, i.e. roughly 2% per year overall

3) All figures at 1980 prices

million unemployed in 1982, the only consequence of a further drop in manufacturing output by the mid 1980s is that still more people are jobless. That assumes that Britain is prepared to put up with all the misery and wasted resources which this entails.

It is simple to devise a different path for the economy. All we do is assume a slightly higher growth rate – an average of two per cent per year from 1976, or total growth between 1976 and 1987 of twenty-three per cent. Such a figure is not particularly ambitious; and with Britain's unused resources (in the shape of the unemployed) plus the clearly unmet demands for products and services, it is difficult to doubt that this figure could be achieved.

In this new assumption (Table 12) primary production expands at the same rate of 119 per cent. The output of manufacturing, construction and services all grow uniformly by around twenty-two per cent over the decade. Meanwhile, expenditure on manufactured goods increases at a slightly higher rate, necessitating a few more imports. The trade balance moves from the deficit of £2.2 billion postulated by Kay and Forsyth to a small surplus. This is hardly anything to worry about. West Germany and Japan existed quite comfortably for years during the 1970s with trade surpluses.

Even if Britain were prepared to put up with high unemployment, the Kay/Forsyth formula would work well enough only for the time North Sea oil insulates Britain from the world outside. But what happens when it runs out? When this happens – in the 1990s or maybe a little later – Britain would have to resurrect the manufacturing industries that it has allowed to decline, to be able to pay for the imports that it needs once more. This could be a slow, costly, heart-rending business. Instead of going through massive structural shifts twice in a generation, it is surely better to ensure that manufacturing remains strong for when Britain needs it urgently again.

Fallacy 2. 'Leave it all to services'

In 1979, Britain exported almost a quarter of its gross domestic product. The total came to some £42 billion worth of commodities, of which manufactured goods contributed £33 billion, together with £14 billion worth of services. The country had to sell overseas if it

Table 13. Britain's exports/imports – 1979 (£ billion)

	Exports	Imports
Commodities		
Food, beverages etc	3·0	6·5
Basic materials	1·2	4·0
Fuels	4·3	5·8
Manufactures	33·0	31·4
Total commodities	41·5	47·7
Services		
Sea transport	3·7	3·7
Civil aviation	1·7	1·4
Travel	2·7	2·1
Financial services	1·6	0
Films/TV	0·1	0·1
Royalties	0·5	0·4
Miscellaneous services	3·2	1·6
Total services	13·5	9·3

was to earn even some of the foreign currency needed to pay for that year's imports (Table 13).

There are two ways of looking at exports and imports. You could say Britain should produce more goods itself and so reduce the need for imports. The other view is that if people in Britain want to splash out on so many foreign items then that is their affair. Whatever happens, however, the imports have to be paid for.

Some people assert that if Britain's manufacturing industry sags and is less able to function as an exporter, then the service sector could expand and earn more from selling overseas to pay for a greater proportion of the exports. If you look at the facts, however, the prospects are far from rosy.

Of the £14 billion worth of services exported, airliners and shippers earned £5.4 billion by collecting fees from foreigners who either travelled with them or sent cargo. There are few prospects for growth here – short of creating a new British Airways or Cunard. In 1979, foreign visitors spent £2.7 billion in the UK, as against the

£2.1 billion that British residents spent abroad. On paper, tourism looks a promising growth industry. Sadly, however, since 1979, the UK tourism business has looked less healthy. From a £600 million trade surplus in 1979 (£400 million less than the year before that), the surplus came to just £208 million in 1980. The travel balance of trade even swung into a £245 million deficit in 1981. It doesn't look as though tourism will turn out much of an export winner either.

Financial and banking services, and royalties on films and so on sold overseas, all look reasonably healthy. But their contribution to the total balance of payments is minimal.

Finally, we have 'miscellaneous services' which accounted for exports worth £3.2 billion. Much of this cash is for duties in connection with North Sea oil and gas production, and could in theory, grow marginally. It also includes computer services in the UK – sales of software, consultancy work and so on. Much has been made of the potential of this kind of work, both for generating sales and employment. Yet in 1979, the UK computer services industry earned little more than a pittance – £450 million. Even if all its customers were foreigners, the industry's export revenue would just about keep Britain in imported clothing and footwear for three months.

Overall, services are extremely unlikely to expand to take over anything but a minuscule part of the export burden that manufacturing industry now shoulders.

Fallacy 3. *Structural unemployment*

Some commentators contend that we are running into a new era in which large sections of the community are permanently without jobs. According to this thesis, the high unemployment of the past few years – both in the UK and elsewhere – is due to some structural defect in the world economy. No improvement is likely, and we should therefore increase unemployment pay and institute other measures to safeguard the welfare of those who cannot get jobs.

This point of view, though well-intentioned, is defeatist. Anyone can see that thousands of jobs need doing. What is lacking, often, is the mechanism to line up supply (of labour) and demand for the products of the work.

Here are some suggestions, made within a couple of months of each other in 1981, about all the work that is crying out to be done.

● The National Economic Development Office's civil engineering committee has called for a £200 million increase in public spending to repair what it calls 'public infrastructure'. The committee is talking about roads, sewers, railways and canals, many of which are falling into disrepair because of lack of resources.

● British Telecom is spending £2 billion per year on replacing the UK's antiquated (by today's standards) telephone network. It would like to spend more, if it could win the government's permission. The work would increase jobs within the UK's electronics industry.

● The Royal Institute of British Architects suggests an £800 million per year programme for twenty years to insulate Britain's houses, save energy and produce 70,000 new jobs.

● A massive £6 billion programme to build houses, reclaim land and provide better transport facilities would make Britain's cities better places and provide 300,000 jobs, says the Association of Metropolitan Authorities.

● According to Friends of the Earth, 60,000 jobs could be created by building cycle ways, insulating houses, collecting waste paper and digging allotments.

● If your taste is for really big schemes, a Department of Energy committee has suggested a barrage across the River Severn to collect energy from the tides. The scheme would cost £5.6 billion over ten years and employ 21,000.

There is no reason why the cash earned by a successful manufacturing industry could not pay for worthwhile schemes such as these – and keep people in work.

The way forward

Automation in industry will be a feature of life over the next few decades. The point is whether Britain wants to have any industry. The country could leave it all to everyone else. Or it could institute a sweeping programme to modernise the country's antiquated factories. The programme would include government cash to strengthen the position of engineers and to introduce technical advances in workshops. Above all the general climate would have to change. People would have to recognise the importance of factory technologies. Everyone appreciates manufactured goods, but few think much about how they are made.

A strong manufacturing industry is the only way Britain can resist the slide into the status of an underdeveloped nation. The change to the new system will not be easy. No one can pretend that automated manufacturing industry will be a big provider of jobs. No one really knows if, in future, services will expand to create the extra jobs lost as the factories automate. But the Japanese experience shows that wealth-creating, though jobs-destroying, manufacturing industry *can* create employment in other sectors of the economy. Britain should try to follow this route. For if it wants to remain a reasonably wealthy nation in the year 2000, there is no other way.

The publisher of this book ought to leave the last few pages blank, to be filled in by the reader at a later date. Robots are still at such an early stage of development that their story is far from complete. Britain has to make up its mind what part it wants to play in that story. On this decision depends whether the country can be moderately hopeful about the future . . . or whether it faces the next few decades with poverty staring it in the face.

Books and reports consulted

Chapter 1

Engineering Our Future, report of committee of inquiry into the engineering profession, chaired by Sir Monty Finniston, HMSO, 1980.

Chapter 2

Man and Automation by Leonard Langdon Goodman, Penguin, 1957.
Automation and Management by James Bright, Harvard University, 1958.

Chapter 3

Automation: the Advent of the Automatic Factory by John Diebold, Van Nostrand, 1952.
Impact of Automation on Employment, report and hearings of the Congressional subcommittee on employment and the impact of automation of the committee on education and labour, US Government Printing Office, 1961.

Chapter 4

Report of the Factory System of the US by Carroll D. Wright, Dept of Interior Printing Office, 1884.
Industrial Archaeology of Britain by R. Buchanan, Allen Lane, 1974.
The Making of the English Working Class by E.P. Thompson, Penguin, 1980.
The Modern Factory System by R. Whately Cooke Taylor, Kegan Paul, 1891.
Introduction to the History of the Factory System by R. Whately Cooke Taylor, Richard Bentley, 1886.
The Industrial Revolution 1760–1840 by T.S. Ashton, Oxford University Press, 1948.
Thomas Newcomen: The Prehistory of the Steam Engine by L.T.C. Rolt, David and Charles, 1963.

Chapter 5

Industry and Empire by E.J. Hobsbawm, Penguin, 1968.
The Boy's Handy Book of the Manufactures and Industries of the World by Elisha Noyce, Ward Locke, 1881.
Victorian Engineering by L.T.C. Rolt, Allen Lane, 1970.
Technology and Society: The Influence of Machines in the United States by S. McKee Rosen and Laura Rosen, Macmillan, 1941.
Reflections on the Decline of Science in England and on Some of its Causes by Charles Babbage, B. Fellowes, 1830.
On the Economy of Machinery and Manufactures by Charles Babbage, Charles Knight, 1832.
History of the American Economy by Ross Robertson, Harcourt Brace, 1955.
My Life and Work by Henry Ford, Heinemann, 1922.
The Modern Factory by George Price, Wiley, 1914.
American Tool Making and Interchangeable Manufacturing by Joseph Woodworth, Page and Co, 1921.
Report of the Factory System of the US by Carroll D. Wright, US Department of Interior Census Office, 1884.

Chapter 6

The Automatic Factory – What Does It Mean? conference proceedings, Institution of Production Engineers, 1955.
Automation, Men and Money, proceedings of 1st British conference on social and economic effects of automation, 1961.
Automation in Business and Industry edited by Eugene Grabbe, Wiley, 1957.
Automation and Economic Progress edited by Howard Bowen and Garth Mangum, Prentice Hall, 1966.
Automation – Friend or Foe? John Campbell, Communist Party, London, 1956.
Automation – Its Purpose and Future by Magnus Pyke, Hutchinson, 1956.
Toward the Automatic Factory by Charles Walker, University Press, 1957.
A Mechanistic or a Human Society? by Walter Wellock, Quinton, 1943.
The Wonder Book of Machinery by Harry Golding, Ward Lock, 1933.
Towards the Automatic Factory: The Economic Consequences of Automation by Paul Einzig, Secker & Warburg, 1956.
Industrial Automatic Controls by Millard Lajoy, Prentice Hall, 1954.
Automation and the Consumer, Conservative Political Centre, 1956.
Numerical Control in Engineering, American Society of Tool and Manufacturing Engineers, McGraw Hill, 1963.

BOOKS AND REPORTS CONSULTED

Manpower Aspects of Automation and Technical Change, OECD, 1966.

Automation: Industrialisation Comes of Age by William Francois, Collier Books, 1964.

Revolution in Miniature by Ernst Braun and Stuart MacDonald, Cambridge University, 1978.

Electronic Computers by S. Hollingdale and G. Toothill, Penguin, 1976

Automation, report by Department of Scientific and Industrial Research, 1956.

The Silicon Chip Book by Peter Marsh, Sphere, 1981.

Player Piano by Kurt Vonnegut, Panther, 1977.

A Soviet Automatic Plant by A. Erivansky, Foreign Languages Publishing House, Moscow, 1955.

Chapter 7

RUR (Rossum's Universal Robots) by Karel Capek, Oxford Paperbacks, 1961.

The Real Book of Robots and Thinking Machines by Julian May, Doubleday, 1961.

The Robots are Among Us by Rolf Strehl, Arco, 1955.

Exploring the World of Robots by Jonathan Rutland, Piccolo, 1978.

Robots: Fact, Fiction and Prediction by Jasia Reichardt, Thames and Hudson, 1978.

Human Robots in Myth and Science by John Cohen, George Allen and Unwin, 1966.

Chapter 8

Joining and Assembly: The Impact of Robots and Automation, report by Advisory Council for Applied Research and Development, HMSO, 1979.

Robotics in Practice, by Joseph Engelberger, Kogan Page, 1980.

Robots in Industry, by G.L. Simons, National Computing Centre, 1980.

Industrial Robots, report by Technical Insights, 1979.

Factory Automation, report by Creative Strategies International, 1981.

Chapter 9

Computer-Controlled Assembly by James Nevins and Daniel Whitney, article in *Scientific American*, Feb. 1978.

Chapter 10

Industrial Robots and Programmable Automation by Wilf Heginbotham, Production Engineering Research Association, 1978.

Industrial Automation – the Automated Factory, report by Creative Strategies International, 1977.

The Factory of the Future, conference proceedings, Infotech, 1979.

Integrated Computer-aided Manufacturing Programme Prospectus, US Air Force, 1979.

The Old World and the New Technologies by Michel Godet and Olivier Ruyssen, EEC Commission, 1980.

Chapter 11

Artificial Intelligence by Sir James Lighthill and others, Science Research Council, 1973.

Interim Report on Study and Research on 5th Generation Computers, Japan Information Processing Development Centre, 1980.

Preliminary Report on Study and Research on 5th Generation Computers, Japan Information Processing Development Centre, 1981.

Principles of Artificial Intelligence by Nils Nillson, Tioga Publishing, 1980.

Artificial Intelligence by Patrick Winston, Addison-Wesley, 1977.

The Robots are Coming – The Implications of Artificial Intelligence Developments, edited by Frank George and John Humphries, National Computing Centre, 1974.

The Handbook of Artificial Intelligence by Avron Barr and Edward Feigenbaum, Pitman, 1981.

Chapter 12

The Human Use of Human Beings by Norbert Wiener, Avon, 1969.

Expert Systems in the Microelectronic Age, edited by Donald Michie, Edinburgh University, 1979.

The Endless Frontier and the Thinking Machine, by Hans Moravec, Stanford University, 1978.

Obstacle Avoidance in the Real World by a Seeing Robot Rover by Hans Moravec, Carnegie-Mellon University, 1980.

Chapter 13

Advanced Automation for Space Missions, A Technical Summary, University of Santa Clara, 1980.

Machine Intelligence and Robotics: Report of the NASA Study Group, NASA, 1980.

182

Extra-Terrestrial Materials Processing and Construction, report of a programme directed by David Criswell, NASA, 1980.
Materials Processing in Space: Early Experiments, NASA, 1980.
2081 by Gerard O'Neill, Jonathan Cape, 1981.
Space Technology edited by Kenneth Gatland, Salamander, 1981.
Robot Explorers by Kenneth Gatland, Blandford Press, 1972.

Chapter 14

Theory of Self Reproducing Automota by John von Neumann, University of Illinois, 1966.
Self Replicating Systems: A Systems Engineering Approach by Georg von Tiesenhausen and Wesley Darbro, NASA, 1980.

Chapter 15

A History of Modern Japan by Richard Story, Penguin, 1979.
Japan as Number 1 by Ezra Vogel, Tuttle Books, Tokyo, 1979.
Japan – the Coming Social Crisis by Jon Woronoff, Lotus Press, Tokyo, 1980.
Management and Industrial Structure in Japan by Naoto Sasaki, Pergamon, 1981.

Chapter 16

The Economics of Technological Progress edited by Tönu Puu and Sören Wibe, Macmillan, 1981.
Technical Innovation and British Economic Performance, edited by Keith Pavitt, Macmillan, 1980.
Technical Change and Employment by Roy Rothwell and Walter Zegfeld, Frances Pinter, 1979.
English Culture and the Decline of the Industrial Spirit 1850–1980 by Martin Wiener, Cambridge, 1981.

Note

Not all the references in the above are to first editions. My thanks to that magnificent institution, the British Library, in which I was able to consult many of the most useful volumes. Thanks are also due to *New Scientist*, in the course of working for which I gleaned much of the information to go into this book; and to Nikki, for putting up with the work that the research and writing has involved.

SMALL IS POSSIBLE

George McRobie

**The sequel to E. F. Schumacher's
SMALL IS BEAUTIFUL
and
A GUIDE FOR THE PERPLEXED.**

The ballast of the wealth of nations has shifted since the late E. F. Schumacher first claimed that small is beautiful, stressing the worldwide human and financial need for 'economics as if people mattered'. The oil crisis predicted by Schumacher has sliced into Western industrial investment. At home and abroad business corporations whose gigantic bulk was mistaken for muscle have staggered to the wall, dinosaur victims of economic evolution. Now more than ever we need to realise the potential of alternative technology and invest in a different tomorrow. In SMALL IS POSSIBLE Schumacher's friend and collaborator George McRobie gives an optimistic progress report from the front line and proves that there *is* an alternative future for all of us.

ECONOMICS   0 349 12307 1   £3.25

THE SCHUMACHER LECTURES

Edited with an introduction by Satish Kumar

With contributions from:

LEOPOLD KOHR   HAZEL HENDERSON   R. D. LAING

EDWARD de BONO   AMORY LOVINS   IVAN ILLICH

JOHN MICHELL   FRITJOF CAPRA

The Schumacher Lectures embraces economics, psychology, physics, linguistics, history and philosophy and brings together eight remarkable and original thinkers with an astonishing range of ideas, which stand as a testimony to the immense influence of E. F. Schumacher's work. The contributors share a common conviction that our society can no longer accept the demands of technology and 'progress' – we must actively determine our destiny and our own real needs.

Satish Kumar is the Chairman of the Schumacher Society and Editor of *Resurgence*, with which Dr Schumacher was closely associated. After Dr Schumacher's death in 1977, *Resurgence* launched the Schumacher Society, which now holds an annual series of lectures in honour of the bestselling author of *Small is Beautiful*.

'A thought provoking and sometimes inspiring taste of the current ideas of some influential thinkers, it is to be recommended.' *Time Out*

PHILOSOPHY   0 349 12118 4   £2.50

Also available on the ABACUS list: